Cradle of Christianity

Cradle of Christianity

Edited by

Yael Israeli and David Mevorah

The Israel Museum, Jerusalem

The Israel Museum, Jerusalem

Cradle of Christianity
Weisbord Exhibition Pavilion
Spring 2000 – Winter 2001

Curators: Yael Israeli and David Mevorah
Assistants to the curators: Arina-Laura Peri,
Natalya Katsnelson, Hagit Maoz
Exhibition designer: Elisheva Yarhi
Associate designer: Pamela Ullman
Traveling exhibitions officer: Carmela Teichman
Assistant curator, traveling exhibition: Naama Vilozny

Editor of the English catalogue: Nancy Benovitz
Editor of the Hebrew catalogue: Efrat Carmon
Translations: David Maisel, Etka Goldstein-Leibowitz
Photographs: Avraham Hay
Photographic editor: Bella Gershovich
Artistic reconstructions: Balage
Drawings: Pnina Arad

Catalogue design: Boulakia, Rausnitz, Souday / Einat Bluhm
Design consultant: Nirit Zur
Production: Boulakia, Rausnitz, Souday / Tzipi Bushari
Technical assistance: Yael Golan, Masha Pozina
Color separations and plates: Shapiro Repro Ltd., Tel Aviv
Printing: Kal Press Ltd., Tel Aviv

Cat. no. 438
ISBN 965 278 265 3

On the cover: Jesus blessing, fragment of a marble relief
from Hanita, 6th century
On the frontispiece: Depictions of saints, part of a wall
painting from Caesarea, 6th–7th century

The exhibition and catalogue were made possible by:

Hans Dichand, Vienna

Zeit-Stiftung, Ebelin und Gerd Bucerius, Hamburg

Bertelsmann-Stiftung, Germany

Schweizer Vereinigung der Freunde des Israel Museums in Jerusalem, Zurich

Dr. Heinrich Grütering, Essen

Verein zur Förderung des Israel-Museums E.V., Berlin

Jeanmaire and Willie Weinstein, San Francisco

Zell Family Fund, Chicago

Weisbord Exhibition Fund

Donors to the Museum's Share 2000 Program

Donors to the 2000 Exhibition Fund: Ruth and Leon Davidoff, Paris
and Mexico City, Hanno D. Mott, New York, The Nash Family Foundation, New
York, and Judy and Michael Steinhardt, New York

Preliminary research for the exhibition was funded by the Kovensky Revolving
Fund for Exhibition Research, South Africa, and the Lady Sieff Fund, U.K.

Lenders to the Exhibition

Israel Antiquities Authority

Staff Archaeological Officer in the Civil Administration of Judea and Samaria

Studium Biblicum Franciscanum Museum, Jerusalem, Custody of Terra Sancta

Musée Sainte-Anne, Pérès Blancs, Jerusalem

Greek Orthodox Patriarchate, Jerusalem

Shlomo Moussaieff, Herzliya and London

The Wolff Family, Jerusalem

Edit Vilensky, Binyamina

Christian Schmidt, Munich

F. J. Dölger-Institut zur Erforschung der Spätantike, Bonn

Dumbarton Oaks, Washington, D.C.

Pierpont Morgan Library, New York

Royal Ontario Museum, Toronto

Staatliche Museen zu Berlin, Skulpturensammlung und
Museum für Byzantinische Kunst

Trustees of the British Museum, London

University of Pennsylvania Museum of Archaeology and Anthropology, Philadelphia

University of Toronto, Malcove Collection

Contents

Foreword

The year 2000, with its accompanying celebrations of the close of one millennium and the start of the next, presented a most appropriate occasion for an exhibition devoted to the archaeological history of Christianity in its land of origin. It was a special honor and privilege for the Israel Museum to be the venue for this important initiative. And as the keepers of the world's foremost collection of the archaeology of the ancient Holy Land, it was perhaps incumbent upon us to prepare and present *Cradle of Christianity* in that momentous year.

Jesus of Nazareth, Pontius Pilate, and the Last Supper – names and events such as these conjure up images of one of civilization's most dramatic stories – that of the birth of Christianity. It was therefore a uniquely challenging undertaking to attempt to illustrate this remarkable history in the Holy Land at the time of Jesus and during the Byzantine period, through an exhibition and catalogue based on finds excavated in our region over the past one hundred fifty years – assembled, interpreted, and presented in a comprehensive manner for the first time.

These subjects have not lost their relevance in these first years of the twenty-first century, when it has become increasingly important to recognize the common roots of all the monotheistic faiths as a way to foster mutual understanding. *Cradle of Christianity* resonates with these principles, and we are therefore especially delighted to be able to recreate this exhibition now for presentation to the American public, in cooperation with the Maltz Museum of Jewish Heritage, Cleveland, Ohio.

I wish to thank the lenders to the exhibition, particularly the Israel Antiquities Authority and the Staff Archaeological Officer in the Civil Administration of Judea and Samaria. I am also grateful to our donors, all of whom are listed elsewhere in this book, whose generous support made our initial production of the exhibition and its accompanying publication possible.

In closing, I wish to pay special tribute to the curators of the exhibition, Yael Israeli, Senior Curator of Archaeology *Emerita*, and David Mevorah, Curator of Hellenistic, Roman, and Byzantine Archaeology, and to all of the Museum staff who assisted them in meeting the important challenges of this undertaking.

James S. Snyder
Anne and Jerome Fisher Director
The Israel Museum, Jerusalem
December 2005

Introduction

The Holy Land occupies an honored position in the storehouse of associations of Christian believers throughout the world, many of whom are familiar with its sites and landscapes even if they never visited the country. This is not surprising, for Christianity played a central role in one of the major chapters in the history of this land: Through the power of Christianity and in its name, commemorative buildings and places of worship were built, roads were laid, and settlements were established. Owing to Christianity, this region, which in the Roman period was little more than a remote province in the eastern part of the Empire, became a focus of world interest and a thriving center. The country's culture and landscape and the spiritual world of its inhabitants two thousand years ago were essential factors in the crystallization of the ideas of Christianity and in the formation of its visual heritage; to a large extent, they were also instrumental in shaping the histories of Europe and the Mediterranean countries, and their influence is still felt today. The beginning of this historical process lies in the figure of Jesus of Nazareth, an itinerant preacher with a charismatic personality and extraordinary powers, who lived most of his short life in the Galilee and spent his final days in Jerusalem.

We know a great deal about the time when Jesus lived – the last century of the Second Temple period – from the writings of Josephus and other ancient historians, and from the extensive excavations carried out in this country, especially in Jerusalem. The literature of the period, which describes life in this land during those fateful days, has enabled us to reconstruct the atmosphere during the time of Jesus and his disciples, to gain a better understanding of the background to his preaching, and to grasp the intense sense of messianic expectation and hope for redemption that prevailed at the time. A reconstruction of the personal history of Jesus, however, is a far more difficult task, for among the stories, legends, and beliefs that have come into being in the course of two thousand years of religious devotion, it is difficult to distinguish between historical reality and the layers of tradition and interpretation that have been added onto it.

Although literary sources attest the existence of Christian communities in this country already in the second half of the first century – that is to say, not long after Jesus' crucifixion – no finds of this period or of the following two hundred years that may be conclusively identified as Christian have been discovered here. Elsewhere, however, there is significant evidence of the beginnings of Christian congregational activity, and Christian artworks of the period have come to light. At Dura Europos in Syria, a Christian baptistery dating from the mid-third century has been discovered, and in burial caves in Rome, first used in the second century, many wall paintings have survived which contain subjects favored by the early Christians. Carved Roman marble sarcophagi are likewise decorated with Christian symbols alongside classical motifs and subjects from the Hebrew Bible.

The earliest finds related to the story of Christianity in the Holy Land date from the fourth century. But from that time onward, for almost four hundred years – the period scholars call the early Byzantine period – Christianity was a dominant factor in the life of the country, and its imprint can be seen in almost every sphere. The abundance of finds bears witness to the spread and consolidation of Christianity and to the economic prosperity it brought, thanks to the generous support of the Byzantine authorities and the widespread phenomenon of pilgrimage to the holy places. Throughout most of this period, Christians were not the majority in the land, but they were undoubtedly an important and influential minority. Jerusalem was almost entirely Christian, but in other regions there were concentrations of people of other faiths: Jews, mainly in the eastern Galilee; Samaritans in the central region and in Samaria; and a large pagan minority in the south. In the seventh century, the eastern Mediterranean became part of the Muslim world, but – as excavations of recent years have revealed – Christian (and Jewish) life went on. Many of the churches remained in use for dozens of years after the Muslim conquest, and the destruction and abandonment that finally overtook them were gradual, the result of the severance of ties with the wealthy heart of the Empire.

The exhibition "Cradle of Christianity" is an attempt to reconstruct, through a synthesis of literary sources and archaeological finds, life in the Christian communities of this country during the first centuries of Christianity. This appears to be the first time that an attempt has been made to assemble such a wide variety of artifacts – architectural elements, ritual objects, personal articles belonging to the inhabitants of the country, and souvenirs made for pilgrims – in a single exhibition. Many of the objects in the exhibition are on view to the public for the first time.

The exhibition is divided into several parts. It begins with a section that provides a glimpse into the world in which Jesus lived some two thousand years ago. The second section is devoted to the structure of the church building and the liturgy, which is presented by means of a reconstruction of the *bema* (presbytery) of a church, complete with its furnishings, ritual objects, and treasures. Another section addresses the topic of monasticism, especially that of the Judean Desert, which was a dominant force in the land during the Byzantine period and which has continued almost uninterruptedly until today. A further section deals with pilgrimage, which was a surprisingly widespread phenomenon at the time, and which shaped, perhaps more than any other factor, the social and economic character of the Holy Land. Finally, a separate section treats the topic of motifs, symbols, and artistic expressions attributable to the Holy Land. These are usually found on small artworks and everyday items, which provide important evidence of life in this land during the early Byzantine period. Though they have received little attention in major museum exhibitions, these modest objects may, in fact, be an echo of the impressive works of art that once decorated the main religious buildings of this land, but which have been lost with the passage of time.

The present publication is organized according to the same themes. Each chapter begins with an article or introduction, followed by sections dealing with specific topics, which are accompanied by photographs and drawings of many of the objects included in the exhibition. Two of the articles were written by eminent scholars in their fields: "The Spread of Christianity in the Holy Land" by Professor Yoram Tsafrir of the Institute of Archaeology, The Hebrew University of Jerusalem, and "The Architecture and Liturgy of the Early Church" by Father Michele Piccirillo, director of Studium Biblicum Franciscanum Museum and head of the Archaeological Expedition to Mt. Nebo in Jordan. At the back of the book, there is a complete catalogue of the objects illustrated in it, including their sources and bibliographic references.

In preparing the exhibition and the accompanying publication, we have tried to present a comprehensive picture of the riches of Christian material culture in the Holy Land. However, as the subject is vast and space is limited, we have only been able to allude to certain interesting topics, such as the relationship between local Christian art and the surrounding Jewish and pagan art, and the degree to which Christian culture borrowed concepts and ideas from Jewish literature. One aspect that we did not address was that of Christian religious doctrine, which took shape in these years, the product of intense theological disputes between the different factions within the Christian world. These disputes, which were to influence the development of the Christian churches in the future, are reflected in ecclesiastical and historical literature. However, where Christian material culture is concerned, it seems that the period in question may be regarded as a single unit and its products as a unified whole. Lack of space has also prevented us from delving into the processes that led to the development of the different manifestations of material culture. Nevertheless, we hope that the picture we have painted, incomplete as it may be, will shed light on the fascinating, flourishing period of the crystallization of Christianity in the Holy Land.

The finds on view in the exhibition required extensive conservation and restoration before they could be presented to the public. Without the dedicated, professional, and talented work of the Israel Museum Laboratories, we would not have been able to mount such a difficult exhibition. We therefore extend our heartfelt thanks to the staff of the Israel Museum Laboratories: David Bigelajzen, Ruth Yekutiel, Adaia Meshorer, Andrei Vainer, Connie Green, Victor Uziel, Ulla Negnavitsky, Paolo Recanati, Marina Rassovsky, Rahel Baharad, Irit Loeb, and Michael Maggen.

The staff of the Israel Antiquities Authority, responsible for conserving and handling the objects – Hava Katz, Chief Curator; Michael Sebanne, Rivka Calderon, Alegre Sevriego, Naomi Sidi, Gabriella Bichovsky, and Donald Ariel, curators; and Jacques Naguer, Raleb Abu Diyab, Hayim Kaftziz, Penina Shor, Michal Druck, Ella Altmark, and Lena Libman, conservators – devoted many days to tracking down material, some of which had lain in storerooms for years, and to registering and skillfully restoring it.

The Staff Archaeological Officer in the Civil Administration of Judea and Samaria, Yitzhak Magen, with the assistance of curator Yoav Tzionit and excavator Shahar Batz, gave us access to very important artifacts and provided detailed and highly valuable information.

We are indebted to the excavators for their enthusiastic cooperation and for allowing us to exhibit material that has not yet been published or which is currently undergoing scientific analysis. Our thanks are extended to: Uzi Dahari, Mordechai Aviam, Claudine Dauphin, Hillel Geva, Eli Shukron, Nurit Feig, Aaron Maeir, Ronny Reich, David Amit, Elat Mazar, Gabi Mazor, Rachel Bar-Natan, Walid Atrash, Yoram Tsafrir, Elias Hamis, Shula Hadad, Gideon Foerster, Joseph Patrich, Zeev Yeivin, Gérald Finkielsztejn, Ehud Netzer, Oren Gutfield, Fanny Vito, Dov Nahlieli, Dina Shalem, Dina Avshalom-Gorney, Ayelet Tacher, Edna Stern, and Yael Gorin-Rosen.

We also thank the many experts who provided us with important advice and information over the course of our research. We are particularly grateful to Yoram Tsafrir, Michele Piccirillo, L. Y. Rahmani, and Leah Di Segni, for their ongoing support and guidance, and to Hayim Goldfus, Vassilios Tzaferis, Yizhar Hirschfeld, Lihi Habas, Rina Talgam, Magen Broshi, and Dan Barag. For the artistic reconstructions we relied on the knowledge and advice of Gideon Avni and John Seligman, and the talents of Benny Arubas and Balage.

Many of the finds related to early Christianity are housed in private collections and museums all over the country; we wish to thank all those who so generously lent their treasures to the exhibition. Several foreign museums also lent objects from their permanent exhibitions, and we are sincerely grateful to them for their cooperation.

In addition, we are indebted to those in charge of the antiquities collections of Jerusalem's Christian institutions: to Roger Merceron and Hermann Konings of Musée Sainte-Anne, Pérès Blancs; to the Greek Orthodox Patriarch, Diodoros I, and the Metropolite Timothy; and to the Studium Biblicum Franciscanum Museum. Special thanks are due to the collectors Shlomo Moussaieff, Herzliya and London, Christian Schmidt, Munich, Lenny Wolff, Jerusalem, and Edit Vilensky, Benyamina, who willingly responded to our requests.

The exhibition was skillfully designed by Elisheva Yarhi, in cooperation with Pamela Ullman, and it was mounted through the devoted assistance of Shlomo Levi, Shabtai Mizrahi, and David Weintraub, along with the technical staff of the Exhibition Design department: Pesach Ruder, Morris Lasry, Menachem Amin, Benjamin Reches, and Ruth Poliakin. The drawings of the motifs appearing on the finds were done by Pnina Arad, and the painted church reconstruction in the exhibition gallery by Yael Kilemnick. From the very outset of this project, we were assisted by the Exhibition and Collection Management department, particularly the Exhibition Budget and Insurance Officer, Dalia Angel, and Henk van Doornik, who handled the myriad details related to loans from abroad.

We are grateful to Efrat Carmon, who was of invaluable assistance in the preparation of the catalogue and also edited the Hebrew version. Our thanks are also extended to Nirit Zur, head of the Publications department, as well as Yael Golan and Masha Pozina, for their helpful contributions to the project. The English edition of the catalogue was edited by Nancy Benovitz, and the translations were done by David Maisel and Etka Goldstein-Leibowitz. Bella Gershovich, photographic editor, organized the many illustrations, and Avraham Hay photographed countless objects tirelessly and with unique talent. Finally, we would like to thank the staff of Boulakia, Rausnitz, Souday, especially Einat Bluhm, for their skillful work on designing and producing this publication.

The entire staff of the Bronfman archaeology wing stood behind us and offered generous assistance at every stage of our endeavor. We are particularly grateful to Silvia Rozenberg, Chief Curator, Adolfo Roitman, Curator of the Shrine of the Book, and to the office staff, Malka Levy, Shira Amsel, and Rotem Arieli, for their assistance and ongoing support.

Finally, we offer our heartfelt thanks to our co-workers Natalya Katsnelson, Arina-Laura Peri, Edna Peretz, Hagit Maoz, and Zadok David, who accompanied us with enthusiasm and boundless dedication all along the route toward the realization of this fascinating and challenging project.

Yael Israeli
Senior Curator
of Archaeology

David Mevorah
Curator of Hellenistic, Roman,
and Byzantine Archaeology

IE'

Concerning Jesus of Nazareth, who was a prophet mighty in deed and word before God and all the people, and how our chief priests and rulers delivered him up to be condemned to death, and crucified him.

Luke 24:19–20

The Historical Jesus

Yael Israeli

Tradition begins the story of Christianity with the birth of Jesus. However, as is often the case with traditions, this story reflects a combination of history and legend, religious interpretation and factual account. Virtually the only sources for the life and personality of the historical Jesus are the books of the New Testament, written in the second half of the first century: that is to say, several decades after Jesus' crucifixion. The authors of these works regarded Jesus as the Messiah, believed in his teachings, and considered it their mission to spread the new faith. They collected oral traditions and early writings that stressed the spiritual dimension of Jesus' life, but were not particularly concerned with historical accuracy.

The New Testament, so called to contrast it with the Hebrew Bible, which Christians call the Old Testament, is a collection of narratives describing the life of Jesus and his group of disciples, as well as letters written by these disciples to the earliest followers. The first four books, known as the Gospels, are ascribed respectively to Matthew, Mark, Luke, and John. The first three of these – the Synoptic Gospels – are largely parallel historical accounts, while the fourth, the Gospel of John, is theological and didactic in nature. The Gospels were written in Greek on the basis of Hebrew and Aramaic sources. Over the course of time, other texts were added to the books of the New Testament, but these were not included in the canonical corpus. Unlike the original books, which are written in a restrained and concise style, the apocryphal compositions are full of detail and embellishment.

Though scholars have attempted to reconstruct the life of Jesus by examining and comparing the different Gospels, the picture that emerges from such an analysis is incomplete. Even Jesus' birthplace and date of birth are not absolutely clear from these sources. Unfortunately, archaeological investigation does not provide specific information about historical figures and their lives; it only sheds light on the material culture of a given period. Nevertheless, it seems that Jesus really lived some two thousand years ago, and that his personality and deeds were the catalyst for all that was to ensue after his death.

Two different versions of the story of Jesus' birth to the Virgin Mary are found in the New Testament, one in the Gospel of Matthew and the other in the Gospel of Luke. Luke describes a census that took place in Judea, for which the members of the population were told to return to their places of origin. That is why Joseph and the pregnant Mary, who lived in Nazareth, traveled to Bethlehem, where Jesus was ultimately born. This census is known, however, to have taken place in 6 CE. Matthew, on the other hand, relates that Joseph and Mary lived in Bethlehem at the time of Jesus' birth. When it was revealed to Herod that the king of the Jews had been born in Bethlehem, Herod grew anxious and ordered the death of all the infants in the vicinity. As a result, Joseph and his family fled to Egypt. On their return to the country they settled in Nazareth, where Jesus was raised. Both versions put Jesus' birthplace in Bethlehem, despite his link to Nazareth, but some scholars think he was born in Nazareth and that the accounts provided by Matthew and Luke were inspired by the desire to link him to the line of David. With regard to the date of Jesus' birth, it seems it was in 4 BCE, at the end of Herod's reign and long before the census.

In contrast to the lack of information about the life of Jesus, we know a great deal about society, government, and daily life in the land during Jesus' time – the period from the end of Herod's reign to the mid-first century CE. This basic picture can be interwoven with what we know about the historical Jesus.

Inscriptions in Hebrew and Greek on ossuaries of the 1st century CE, attesting to the popularity of the names of Jesus, his family, and his disciples among the Jewish population of Palestine during this period. Above: Jesus / Jesus son of Joseph, Judas son of Jesus. Opposite: Martha, Mary, Matthew, Judas, Jesus son of Alot.

Herod the Great died in 4 BCE. Immediately after his death, serious disturbances broke out that were cruelly suppressed by Varus, the Roman governor of Syria. Herod had bequeathed his kingdom to his three sons: The regions of Judea, Samaria, and Idumea were given to Archelaus; Galilee and Perea (in Jordan) to Herod Antipas; and Auranitis (in Syria) to Philip. But the Roman emperor, Augustus, withdrew the title of king from Archelaus, leaving him with the title of ethnarch only. In 6 CE, after repeated complaints from Jews and Samaritans alike, Archelaus was deposed, and his area of rule became a Roman province. The new province, governed by a Roman prefect, was named *Provincia Judaea*, and its capital was Caesarea.

The prefect (or procurator, as he was also called later) had both military and juridical authority. He also administered financial affairs. In order to determine the amount of tax – poll tax and land tax – to be collected from the inhabitants of the province, it was necessary to conduct a census every few years. In addition, custom dues were levied at the frontier posts by tax collectors.

The tax collectors gained wealth and power through their position, but Jewish society regarded them as socially inferior. This may be the reason why Jesus is said to have befriended them.

Within the Roman system of rule, the local government had, relatively speaking, a great deal of autonomy. Preserving order, raising taxes, and dispensing justice on the lower levels remained the responsibility of the Sanhedrin, which was also the supreme authority in religious matters and in matters pertaining to the Temple. The members of the Sanhedrin came from all parts of the country and from all social strata, with priests and sages among them. The Sanhedrin was headed by the high priest, who was appointed from among a few families of the ruling aristocracy – the Sadducees – whose position enabled them to accumulate great wealth. The Sadducees were conservative in their outlook; they adhered to the Written Law and were disdainful of the Oral Law. In contrast, the sages, who were not necessarily from the upper classes, regarded the Oral Law as essential for the interpretation of the Written Law and for teaching actual conduct in daily life. In the first century BCE, the power and influence of the sages increased, and they won popularity in many circles, becoming the leaders of the largest segment of Jewish society – the Pharisees. Among the Pharisees were also extremist factions that wished to wage a war of liberation against the Roman conquerors. The Zealots, who raised the standard of revolt at the end of the Second Temple period, came from their ranks.

Another faction within Jewish society, with a well-organized structure and a sect-like character, were the Essenes, whose members lived an ascetic, communal existence, were scrupulous about the laws of purity, and disdained the accumulation of wealth and possessions. The principles of the sect and its way of life have become apparent to us chiefly through the discovery of the Dead Sea Scrolls in caves above the Dead Sea, near the ancient settlement at Khirbet Qumran. The inhabitants of this settlement were apparently Essenes. From their writings, we have learned of the extremist nature of the group, whose members, most of whom were priests, chose to cut themselves off from the rest of Jewish society and live in the desert.

Many concepts of the Dead Sea sect recall the ideas of early Christianity; their resemblance to the teachings of John the Baptist is particularly striking. John was the same age as Jesus, and according to the Gospels (Luke 1), he and Jesus were related. The little we know about John is that he was born in Ein Kerem, near Jerusalem, and when he grew up, he went off to live in the Judean Desert. He advocated asceticism and preached repentance, which he symbolized through baptism in the Jordan River: "I baptize you with water for repentance" (Matthew 3:11). John, who was active a short time before Jesus, warned of the approaching Day of Judgement and of the bitter fate in store for those who would not repent of their deeds and renounce their evil ways. He had many followers, and even Jesus came to be baptized by him. The authorities feared that the preachings of John the Baptist would incite popular unrest, and Herod Antipas, ruler of Galilee and Perea, whom John had condemned for marrying his brother's wife, Herodias, had him beheaded (Matthew 14).

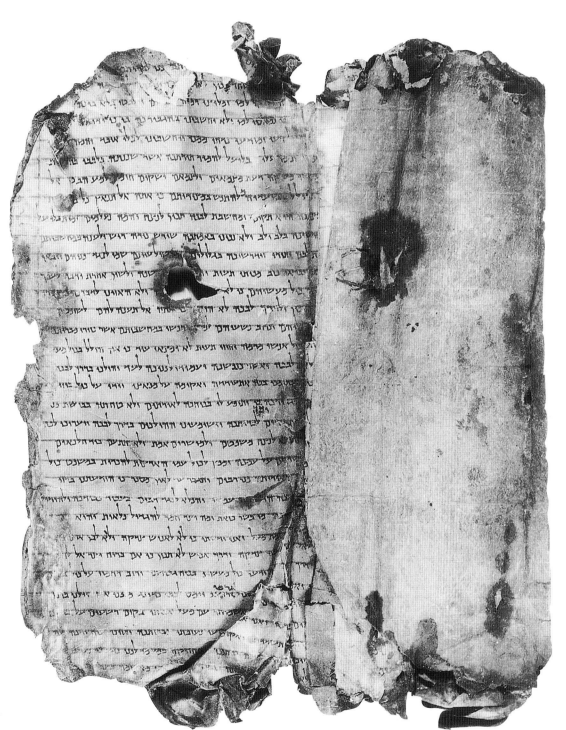

The Thanksgiving Scroll, one of the Dead Sea Scrolls of the 1st century CE that expresses religious views similar to those found in Christianity after Jesus.

Opposite:
A corner in the exhibition, with jars of the type referred to in the story of the Marriage at Cana: "On the third day there was a marriage at Cana in Galilee, and the mother of Jesus was there; Jesus also was invited to the marriage, with his disciples ... Now six stone jars were standing there, for the Jewish rites of purification ..." (John 2:1–6).
The large stone jars pictured here, excavated throughout Jerusalem, date from the 1st century CE. Stone vessels were particularly popular in the Late Second Temple period, for according to Jewish law, stoneware does not contract impurity.

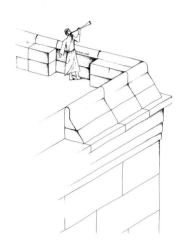

Fragment of a parapet that surrounded the Temple enclosure, bearing a carved Hebrew inscription: "To the place of trumpeting to de[clare?] . . ." It fell from the southwestern corner of the Temple Mount, where the priests stood to announce with trumpet blasts the beginning and end of the Sabbath. Reference to the Temple's great height is found in the story of the Temptation of Jesus: "Then the devil took him to the holy city, and set him on the pinnacle of the temple, and said to him: 'If you are the Son of God, throw yourself down . . .'" (Matthew 4:5–6).

Jesus grew up in Nazareth, which in his time was a small village. He began his activities in the Galilee, mainly in the settlements along the northern shore of the Sea of Galilee, which was a flourishing agricultural area: "For the land is everywhere so rich in soil and pasturage and produces such variety of trees . . . In fact, every inch of the soil has been cultivated by the inhabitants" (Josephus, *Jewish War*, III. 42–43). Jesus traveled about this region, particularly in the Gennesar Valley, teaching and preaching in synagogues and everywhere a crowd gathered. His audience consisted of simple people: artisans, fishermen, and farmers, and his first disciples came from their ranks. The Gospels mention some of the villages through which Jesus passed, such as Capernaum, Migdal, Chorazin, and Bethsaida. It would seem that Jesus deliberately refrained from entering the large towns in the area, Sepphoris and Tiberias. The accounts of Jesus in the Galilee abound in stories of healing and miracles. He purposely associated with sinners and stressed God's love and compassion for all. In his "Sermon on the Mount" (Matthew 5–7), he expounded the principles of his moral teachings, claiming that he had not come to deny the teachings of the prophets but to fulfill them. He called for loving one's enemy, frugal living, and the avoidance of anger and strife; he attacked hypocrisy and pretence and forbade divorce. Jesus asked his followers to abandon everything and follow him. He had twelve disciples or "apostles" – a symbolic number, corresponding to the twelve tribes of Israel.

It was probably in the year 30 that Jesus and his disciples traveled to Jerusalem for the Passover festival. We do not know which route they took: through Samaria and the central hill country, or through the Jordan Valley. In any case, they entered Jerusalem from the east, via Jericho. According to the Gospels, Jesus knew what was in store for him and went in full knowledge of his fate. His last days in Jerusalem were replete with symbolic acts: he entered the city mounted on an ass and spent his time in and around the Temple. Owing to the festival, Jerusalem was filled with pilgrims, and the Temple area thronged with people. Performing the commandment of pilgrimage, bringing tithes and offerings, and paying the Temple taxes all involved money and commerce, and thus the nearby streets and perhaps even the Temple courtyard were full of hawkers and moneychangers, besides the various merchants who were presumably always to be found in the city's hub. A famous symbolic gesture ascribed to Jesus was expelling the moneychangers and the merchants, whom he saw as defiling the House of Prayer. He overturned their tables, perhaps also prefiguring the future

Fragmentary Greek inscription, part of a sign found in Jerusalem, which forbids entry to the Temple. Josephus relates that there were many inscriptions, "some in Greek, others in Latin," warning foreigners against proceeding past the balustrade that surrounded the Temple's inner court (*Jewish War*, V. 193). This balustrade demarcated the sacred area to which Jews were permitted to enter only after they had undergone ritual purification. A complete inscription of this type was discovered in Jerusalem in the 19th century and is currently on view in the Archaeological Museum of Istanbul. It enabled the reconstruction of the inscription, as follows: "No foreigner shall enter within the balustrade of the Temple, or within the precinct, and whosoever shall be caught shall be responsible for (his) death that will follow in consequence (of his trespassing)." This was the only instance in which the high priest had the authority to exercise the death penalty, without handing the transgressor over to the Roman procurator for trial.

Ossuary of "Joseph son of Caiaphas" the high priest. The burial cave of the Caiaphas clan was found in southeastern Jerusalem. It contained twelve ossuaries, one of which, bearing the name "Joseph son of Caiaphas," was the most elaborate of them all. The full name appearing twice on the ossuary and the high quality of the decoration support the assumption that the deceased was indeed the Joseph Caiaphas mentioned in conjunction with the story of Jesus. This is the only case in which an ossuary bearing the name of a prominent historical figure has been discovered.

...]s Tiberievm
... pon]tivsPilatvs
.. praef]ectvslvda[ea]e

Latin dedicatory inscription carved in stone, found in secondary use in the theater of Caesarea. This is the only known archaeological find bearing the name of Pontius Pilate, the fifth Roman procurator of Judea (26–36 CE), who sentenced Jesus to death by crucifixion. Until the discovery of this inscription, our knowledge of Pilate was based entirely on literary sources. The stone was originally set in a building constructed in Caesarea by Pilate in honor of the Emperor Tiberius.

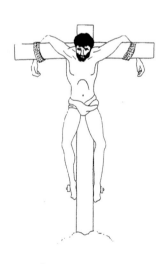

Suggested reconstruction of the crucifixion of Yehohanan son of Hagkol

destruction of the Temple, of which he prophesized: "there will not be left here one stone upon another" (Matthew 24:2). While Jesus was in the Temple, he taught the public and disputed with the Pharisaic sages, making a great impression on his audience.

Messianic expectations played a central role in Jewish religion at the end of the Second Temple period, and the atmosphere was fraught with social and religious tensions and eschatological longings. The exchanges between Jesus and the others in the Temple, as recorded in the Gospels, allude to the disputes between the different factions within Jewish society concerning the coming of the Messiah, the resurrection of the dead, and the Kingdom of Heaven. These issues lay at the heart of Jesus' teachings. Jesus prophesized that the Kingdom of Heaven was close at hand, and that the time would come when all mankind would live an ideal existence on earth. He saw himself as God's representative, calling himself the "Son of man" and referring to God as "my Father," and it would seem, though this is not said specifically, that he believed himself to be the Messiah.

In Jerusalem, Jesus and his disciples held a festive meal, perhaps the Passover seder. Jesus pronounced the blessings over the wine and bread and offered them to his disciples, saying that the bread was his flesh and the wine his blood. These words would later become the basis of the Christian Eucharist. The meal took place on a Thursday night. Later that evening, Jesus was arrested by representatives

of the high priest Joseph Caiaphas, apparently because his remarks concerning the fall of the Temple were viewed as incitement. After a trial at which witnesses came forward to accuse him, Jesus was handed over to the Roman procurator Pontius Pilate. (Owing to the festival and the masses of pilgrims in the city, Pilate was in Jerusalem at the time rather than in Caesarea, his seat of residence.) This is the only part of the story of Jesus' life in which historical figures are mentioned whose existence has been confirmed by literary sources outside the Gospels and by archaeological finds. On Friday, Pontius Pilate sentenced Jesus to death by crucifixion. This was a cruel and humiliating method of execution, which was used in many parts of the ancient world and was accompanied by various forms of torture, depending on the cruelty of the executioners. The Romans used to crucify only the most serious criminals, generally those who were perceived as threats to their rule.

Jesus was crucified together with two thieves. Owing to the commencement of the Sabbath that evening, Pilate allowed Jesus to be taken down from the cross and buried the same day. Joseph of Arimathea, "a member of the council, a good and righteous man" buried Jesus in a rock-hewn tomb he had dug for himself. When the Sabbath ended, "Mary Magdalene and the other Mary," women who had followed Jesus to Jerusalem from the Galilee, found that the stone used to block the entrance to the tomb had been rolled away and that the tomb was empty (Mark 16:1–6).

In Josephus's *Jewish Antiquities*, dating from the end of the first century, Jesus is mentioned in two places. These passages are believed to be inauthentic, either a later reworking of the text or even a forgery. But in a tenth-century Arabic translation of this work, there is a summary which may indeed have been written by Josephus: "At this time there was a wise man called Jesus. His conduct was good and he was known to be virtuous. And many people from among the Jews and the other nations became his disciples. Pilate condemned him to be crucified and to die. But those who had become his disciples did not abandon him. They reported that he had appeared to them three days after his crucifixion, and that he was alive; accordingly he was considered to be the Messiah, concerning whom the prophets have recounted wonders."

Heel bone punctured by an iron nail (above, left), the only tangible evidence of the practice of crucifixion to have been discovered in archaeological excavations. The bone was found within an ossuary in a cave in north Jerusalem. The deceased, whose name – Yehohanan son of Hagkol – is inscribed on the ossuary (above, right), was a young Jew in his twenties. The find indicates that his legs had been nailed to the sides of the cross, while his arms were apparently tied to the crossbeam. When his body was taken down for burial, presumably by members of his family, they were unable to detach his right foot from the pole, since the nail was bent, and so they also removed part of the wooden cross, which remained attached to the heel bone by the nail.

I

And Jesus came and said to them, "All authority in heaven and on earth has been given to me. Go therefore and make disciples of all nations, baptizing them in the name of the Father and of the Son and of the Holy Spirit."

Matthew 28:18–19

Previous page: Dome of the apse in the
church of St. Catherine's Monastery, Sinai

The Spread of Christianity in the Holy Land

Yoram Tsafrir

According to the Book of Acts, the first Christian community settled in Jerusalem after Jesus' death and resurrection. Jesus revealed himself to the people of this community once again after his ascent to Heaven, and several days later, they saw him ascending to Heaven for a second time (thus dispelling any doubts concerning his death and resurrection). The first Christian community was composed of Jesus' disciples as well as other Jews who believed in his resurrection and in the Second Coming. Simon-Peter and James, Jesus' brother, were the community's leaders. These first Christians were rejected and even persecuted by the Jewish leadership of Jerusalem. Several years after Jesus' death, Stephen, one of the members of this community, was stoned to death. He was subsequently recognized as the first in a series of martyrs who sacrificed their lives for the sake of Christian belief.

Sometime later, a zealous Jew named Saul – Paul the Apostle – joined the community. According to the Book of Acts, Paul had participated in anti-Christian persecutions, but was struck blind and, after experiencing a revelation, was converted into a faithful Christian. Paul was born in the city of Tarsus in Cilicia (now southeastern Turkey). He therefore had much in common with the Jews of the Diaspora and was familiar with the lifestyle and beliefs of the non-Jews living in the Hellenistic East. Paul played a decisive role in the dissemination of Christianity among pagans when he decided to forgo the prerequisite of conversion to Judaism. This step made it easier for pagans throughout the Roman Empire to embrace Christianity, for they could now join the new religion, which offered spiritual messages and the promise of personal redemption, without being forced to take on the stringent requirements of Judaism – circumcision, the observance of dietary restrictions (kashrut), and so forth. Paul and his associates, and to a lesser extent other Apostles, such as Peter, spread the faith among Jews and pagans throughout the Hellenistic East, even as far as Rome. Although Christianity continued to be disseminated vigorously throughout Palestine during the second half of the first century CE, most of the activity took place in the Diaspora.

Churches and Monasteries
of the Holy Land in the
Byzantine Period

Christianity's demand that its followers be faithful to Jesus and his teachings, without any concession to Imperial cult, caused a deep rift between Christianity and the Empire. The citizens of the Empire and the emperors themselves were not averse to accepting new cults in addition to the numerous cults that already existed within the polytheistic Empire. The emperors merely insisted that its citizens express their loyalty to the Empire and its rulers by participating in the Imperial cult and offering sacrifices on behalf of the Emperor's welfare. The Christians refused to obey this demand, and Christianity was consequently perceived as a threat to the very existence of the Empire and its rule. At times, the Empire reacted by persecuting Christians, often by execution. The martyrs – those who died for their beliefs – were glorified and became Christian saints. Both Peter and Paul are said to have been executed by the Romans because of their faith.

As long as the Empire preserved its power and the emperors' position was not weakened, the new religion, though it continued to grow at a steady pace, did not threaten the Empire's internal unity. Matters changed greatly, however, in the second century and particularly the third century. By this period, classical polytheism had already lost its prestige and appeal, and it was difficult to convince the masses of the supernatural power and moral superiority of stone and wooden gods. For this reason, the popularity of mystical religions, such as the cult of Isis, which originated in Egypt, the cult of Mithras, from Persia, and the cult of the Great Mother, Cybele, from Asia Minor, increased. Paganism's main rivals for the souls of the Empire's inhabitants were Judaism and Christianity. Both emphasized the spiritual rewards that converts would receive in exchange for forgoing various pleasures and even risking social ostracism. But Christianity enjoyed a great advantage over Judaism, since it did not require circumcision and observance of the commandments; moreover, an important position was allotted to women within the community structure. Conversion to Christianity was accompanied by a feeling of personal sacrifice, of common destiny, and of mutual responsibility. In the third century, when the Empire plunged into a period of crisis that threatened its very existence, and its citizens lost their sense of personal security, Christianity grew particularly powerful. In such an unstable world, affiliation with the Christian congregations gave the individual a certain sense of security, and the promise of personal redemption lent meaning, even to the period of suffering. When, in the late third century, Rome finally emerged from the crisis, large and powerful Christian communities had already been established throughout the Roman Empire. The waves of persecution against Christians that took place during this period did not inhibit the continued growth of these communities.

In Judea, Christianity underwent similar developments. Although at first the Christians viewed themselves as Jews, they broke with Jewish destiny by abandoning Jerusalem on the eve of the revolt against the Romans (66–70), which ended with Jerusalem's destruction. The very destruction of Jerusalem and the Temple was interpreted as the fulfillment of Jesus' prophecy. Our knowledge of this period is mainly based upon a book written by the Church Father Eusebius, who was active in Caesarea at the end of the third and the beginning of the fourth century. Eusebius relates that Christians returned to Jerusalem after the destruction, and he lists the names of the bishops – the

Mosaic from the
dome of the apse
in the church of
St. Catherine's
Monastery, Sinai,
6th century

"overseers" or community leaders – who had officiated from the time of James, the brother of Jesus, until his day. The first bishops were Judeo-Christians (members of the "church from the circumcision"), but from the time of the Bar Kokhba Revolt, following which the Emperor Hadrian prohibited Jews from residing in Jerusalem, Christians who had no connection with Judaism (members of "the church from the Gentiles") served in the city as bishops.

Initially, the majority of the members of the new faith in Palestine were Judeo-Christians, who believed (in opposition to Paul) that affiliation with the Jewish religion and observance of the commandments were prerequisites for Christian faith. Such people are probably the *minim* (apostates) mentioned in Jewish sources, whom the Jewish leaders vehemently opposed. In the hellenized cities, of course, uncircumcised Christians formed the majority. Although literary evidence points to the presence of Judeo-Christians and Christians in Palestine in the first centuries CE, archaeology has not, to date, been able to identify with certainty the remains of religious structures or objects belonging to the first Christians in this land prior to the fourth century. At Capernaum (north of the Sea of Galilee), a large structure from the first centuries CE, identified as the "House of St. Peter," was discovered beneath the remains of a fifth century church. The excavators believe that the structure served as the house of prayer (*domos ecclesiae*) of the first Christians. Although such an explanation is possible, it is by no means the only interpretation. Examples of Christian congregational buildings have, however, come to light in other lands. For example, a Christian building from the third century was discovered in the city of Dura Europos on the Euphrates; buildings of the Christian congregations were also unearthed beneath fourth–fifth century churches in Rome, and Christian symbols were found in the city's catacombs. The lack of Christian finds from Palestine before the fourth century does not point to the absence of Christians in the country, but rather, to the inability of archaeology to identify their remains.

A dramatic change in the status of Christianity occurred during the first half of the fourth century. Following Constantine's victory and his ascension to the throne as the sole emperor (324), a new era began in the history of the Roman Empire. Already in 313, Constantine had conferred upon the Christians, his allies in his struggle for rule, the status of members of a "permitted religion," and the persecutions against them ceased. Around that time, the first basilical churches were built – one in Rome (today, San Giovani on the Lateran Hill) and the other in Tyre. Christianity had triumphed, and it began to attract masses of people. Over the course of the fourth century, it became the official and mandatory religion of the Empire. In 330, the capital was transferred from Rome to Constantinople (previously called Byzantium). Many scholars therefore assign the beginning of Christian rule to this year, and the period is referred to as the "Byzantine period." At the end of the fourth century, laws were enacted that called for the destruction of pagan temples throughout the Empire, and pagan cults were forbidden. Jews and Samaritans were tolerated, since they too were monotheists and worshiped God the Father, but strong pressure was exerted upon them to convert to Christianity.

Ostracon bearing the text of the Christian creed, written in Greek on both sides. In the Creed, the believer declares his faith in the nature of Jesus, who was incarnate from the Holy Spirit and the Virgin Mary, suffered and was crucified by Pontius Pilate, and rose again on the third day. He also states his belief in the Church, in one Baptism for the forgiveness of sins, in the resurrection of the dead, and in the life of the age to come (the afterlife). The formula of the Creed was fixed in the Councils of Nicea and Constantinople (325 and 381 CE). The ostracon may have been used to help catechumens memorize the text.

The process of Christianization was particularly swift in Palestine. The province of *Palaestina*, with Caesarea as its capital, had previously been just another Roman province. Following Constantine's conquest of the East, however, it became the Holy Land – the country of Jesus' birth, death, and resurrection. The places associated with Jesus came to be regarded holy sites; they were cultivated by Christians, and upon them churches were erected. Vigorous efforts to Christianize the population commenced throughout the Holy Land, primarily in Jerusalem and Bethlehem, and in other sites where Jesus was active – in the vicinity of the Sea of Galilee and in the Lower Galilee. Pilgrimage to the holy sites reached tremendous proportions already in the first stages of Christian rule. The most outstanding example of pilgrimage is that of Empress Helena, mother of Constantine, who arrived in Jerusalem in ca. 326. Tradition attributes the discovery of Jesus' tomb to her, though the actual excavation work was carried out on Constantine's orders, undoubtedly under the inspiration of Macarius, bishop of the Christian community in Jerusalem.

Around the year 33 CE, when Jesus was crucified on the hillock of Golgotha and buried nearby, his tomb lay outside Jerusalem's city wall (the Second Wall). However, when the tomb was discovered in the fourth century, it was located in the center of Aelia Capitolina – Roman Jerusalem. Above the presumed site – the memory of which had been preserved by Christians for hundreds of years – stood a Roman temple. The Christians claimed that the Romans intentionally built a temple to the pagan goddess Aphrodite over the site in order to hide the life-giving tomb, though this is doubtful. In order to reveal the tomb, it was necessary to tear down the temple and remove the foundation

Ornamented cross (*crux gemmata*). The quadrants bear Christograms (IC, XC) and the first and last letters of the Greek alphabet (Α, ω). Painting on plaster, discovered in a granary beneath the governor's palace in Caesarea, 6th century.

on which it had been built. The discovery of the tomb inspired the Emperor to order the construction of a magnificent Christian basilica at the site, in order to glorify the miracle of the resurrection. The church, dedicated in 335, became a symbol of the triumph of Christianity. Overlooking it from the east was the Temple Mount, where the Temple lay in ruins. This came to represent the historical Jerusalem, which had been destroyed, while the Church of the Holy Sepulcher was seen as the True Temple and the New Jerusalem.

Eusebius, who had personally witnessed Christianity's transformation from a persecuted sect to the official religion of the Empire, records that the Emperor Constantine, whom he regarded as the Apostles' successor in the mission of disseminating Christianity, also built churches at other Christian holy sites: on the summit of the Mount of Olives (the Eleona Church); above the Cave of the Nativity in Bethlehem; and at Mamre, near Hebron, where Abraham received the tidings of the birth of his son Isaac from the angels. During this period, the principal models for church edifices were formulated – both for the churches that served the various Christian congregations, which were usually elongated basilicas, and for those that, aside from being used for prayers, also served as commemorative structures at the holy sites. The latter were frequently round, octagonal, or cruciform in plan, with the raised, central section glorifying the holy place.

The Christianization of the polytheistic population of the Holy Land transpired relatively quickly. Since the worship of classical gods had lost its appeal long before, whereas Christianity, once it became the official religion of the Empire, could offer evidence of its validity and success, Christianity became the religion that was perceived as worthwhile to embrace. In contrast, the new faith encountered opposition in areas of Jewish settlement, such as the Galilee and the vicinity of Tiberias, and in the region of Samaria, where the Samaritans lived. It was easier to introduce Christianity in the large cities of the coastal region, in those east of the Jordan River, and even in the cities of Judea, where the Jewish community had been annihilated and replaced by pagans in the wake of the Bar Kokhba Revolt (132–135). Jerusalem itself was forbidden to Jews (though a small Jewish community continued to exist there), and thus it too could easily be converted into a Christian city.

During the second half of the fourth century, the pace of Christianization was accelerated throughout the entire Roman world. Toward the end of the century (ca. 391), the Emperor Theodosius I prohibited the worship of pagan gods and decreed that all heathen temples must be shut down and destroyed. It appears that locally, the process was even faster, as this was the Holy Land. Around 400, the great temple of the god Marnas in Gaza, the last pagan stronghold, was laid to waste (other pagan temples in the city had been shut down previously). After the site had been cleansed and purified, a large church was erected there, with the support of the Empress Eudoxia. This event symbolized the final surrender of paganism, although it may be presumed that here and there, individuals and communities continued to adhere to the old beliefs. The Church's strength increased, and its leaders held many positions of social and spiritual authority in villages and cities. Pilgrims flooded the region from all over the world, which encouraged the discovery of additional holy sites and relics. The number of monks also grew; some lived in villages or cities, particularly in Jerusalem, but the most highly esteemed were those who retreated to the solitude of the Judean Desert and Sinai. The Christian leadership came mainly from their ranks, and they played an important role in shaping the Holy Land's spiritual and religious character.

In the Byzantine period (4th–7th century), the land reached its demographic peak (to which it did not return until the first half of the twentieth century). The cities grew in size and population, and many regions that had previously only been sparsely populated, such as the central Negev, were now filled with settlements. Caesarea continued to serve as the administrative capital, but Jerusalem, with the church of Zion, "the mother of all churches," was the most important city. In 451 it became the capital of the Fifth Patriarchate, alongside Constantinople, Rome, Antioch, and Alexandria. The number of churches steadily increased (as did, though on a smaller scale, the number of synagogues), and we know of some settlements that contained numerous churches.

Gethsemane and the
Mount of Olives in the
mid-19th century

Christian rule and the central role played by the Church leaders in each community led to a gradual change in the face of cities and in daily life. The governors of the provinces, who represented the Emperor, and the city councils and citizen associations, which had been the basis of urban rule during the Roman period, lost most of their power, whereas the power of the Church leadership increased. The place of social assembly was transferred from the forum and public buildings, principally the civic basilica, to churches and their forecourts. Theater performances, which dealt (even if satirically) with the Greek gods, ceased in the fifth century, or, at the very latest, in the beginning of the sixth century, and the statues that once graced the cities' streets, squares, and public edifices vanished from view. Despite the attempts of those devoted to the classical heritage to preserve its literary and artistic spirit, the classical tradition gradually disappeared. Certain leisure institutions that were somewhat less identified with pagan culture, however, such as the bathhouse and chariot racing, continued to function.

Social and communal life, like the life of the individual, revolved around the religious institutions. The most prominent writers were members of the ecclesiastical leadership, such as the Church Fathers Eusebius and Jerome. The former composed a history of the Church in Greek, as well as numerous works devoted to commentary and theology. The latter, who lived in a monastery in Bethlehem (ca. 385–420) and was one of the most prolific Latin authors of all times, wrote a Latin translation of the Holy Scriptures (the Vulgate), commentaries on the Bible and the New Testament, as well as philosophical and theological treatises. The works of art that decorated the churches (and synagogues too), particularly frescoes and mosaics, expressed the individual's spiritual needs and aesthetic sensibilities, as well as the Church leaders' didactic aims. We are principally familiar with the floor mosaics, since they are better preserved than the frescoes and wall mosaics, most of which have been destroyed. An outstanding example of the latter is the magnificent mosaic in the church of St. Catherine's Monastery in Sinai, which portrays Jesus' transfiguration from a man to God and back. In this work, Jesus is shown standing between the prophets Moses and Elijah, surrounded by portraits of other prophets and the Apostles. The frescoes of this church depict the Sacrifice of Isaac and the Daughter of Jephthah – offerings that preceded Jesus' own sacrifice. Portable art works, such as icons of saints painted on wood, ceremonial vessels, and *eulogia* amulets, complete the assemblage of Christian art from this period.

In the second half of the sixth century, the Byzantine Empire began to decline. The continuous wars against the Sassanian Persians weakened the Empire's army and economy, the effects of which were also felt in the Holy Land. In 614, the Sassanians conquered Jerusalem and slaughtered or expelled most of its inhabitants. They even seized the remnants of the True Cross, the most important Christian relic. During the period of conquest, when communication between the administrative center in Constantinople and the provinces was severed, the leadership of the community naturally fell to the local authorities, namely, the religious leaders. Although the Byzantines managed to reconquer the province of Palestine and Jerusalem some fourteen years later, and the True Cross was returned to its place in the Church of the Holy Sepulcher, Byzantine rule was never fully restored. Within a few years (630–640), the Holy Land fell to the Muslims.

A Christian population continued to exist in the Holy Land even under Muslim rule, with leadership of the Christian communities remaining in the hands of the bishops and local church heads. The impact of Christian rule on the Holy Land was to be felt for generations to come, and lifestyles, prayers, and religious practices, as well as many churches and monasteries, that were established during the Byzantine period can still be observed today.

1   2   3   4   5

The decorations really are too marvellous for words . . . and so is the magnificent building itself. It was built by Constantine, and under the supervision of his mother it was decorated with gold, mosaic, and precious marble, as much as his empire could provide . . .

Egeria's Travels, 25.9

The Church of the Holy Sepulcher

The Church of the Holy Sepulcher was the most important of the Christian sites in the Holy Land. Eusebius, bishop of Caesarea, relates in his *Life of Constantine* that the Emperor built commemorative structures and houses of prayer at the sites of three caves associated with major events in the life of Jesus. One of these was the Church of the Holy Sepulcher, situated above the site of Jesus' crucifixion and the nearby cave where he was buried. Eusebius provides a detailed account of the construction of the three-part church complex, which was built in strict accordance with the Emperor's instructions: First, the pagan temple that stood on the site was removed. Next, the cave was made into an independant structure (later surrounded by a spacious, round domed hall – the Rotunda); following this, a peristyle courtyard was constructed, in the corner of which stood the rock of Golgotha (the traditional site of the Crucifixion), surmounted by a large cross; finally, a vast basilica, called the Martyrium, was erected, containing four aisles, two on each side of the central nave. Parts of the church have remained unchanged since the Byzantine period, while others have been altered, particularly in the time of the Crusades. The reconstructed plan of the Byzantine church that is accepted today is based on the remains of walls discovered in excavations and on literary descriptions from that period.

The Church of the Holy Sepulcher was regarded as the center of the universe. Within the basilica was the cave in which the remains of the True Cross were said to have been found, as well as the church treasury, where the sacred relics, displayed to pilgrims during special ceremonies, were stored. The most important of these relics were the remains of the True Cross. There was also a sign bearing the inscription "King of the Jews," which according to tradition, was placed above Jesus' head at the time of the Crucifixion, as well as the chalice Jesus used at the Last Supper. In addition to these objects, the treasury also contained King Solomon's signet ring, with which he overcame demons, and the horn of oil used for anointing the kings of Judah.

Opposite: Reconstruction of the Church of the Holy Sepulcher in the 6th century. Above: Exterior view. Below: An artist's proposal for the reconstruction of the interior. The painting includes later additions to Constantine's original building. Apart from the rock of Golgotha, few remains of the Byzantine church have survived above ground. The reconstruction is based on literary descriptions from Byzantine times and scholars' suggestions. The details of the furniture and ornamentation are also derived from literary sources, and from surviving wall mosaics, mainly those in the churches of Ravenna in northern Italy.

1. Rotunda (Anastasis)
2. Sepulcher (Aedicula)
3. Courtyard
4. Gologtha (Calvary)
5. Basilica

At midday they go before the Cross – whether it is rain or fine, for the place is out of doors – into the very spacious and beautiful courtyard between the Cross and the Anastasis . . .

Egeria's Travels, 37. 4

Golgotha

The place where Jesus was crucified was called Golgotha, a Greek corruption of the Hebrew word for skull (*golgolet*); the name is still used today (together with the Latin name "Calvary"). Tradition identifies the site as the rock in the center of the Church of the Holy Sepulcher, which in the Byzantine period stood in the corner of an open courtyard surrounded by columns. The rock was surmounted by a large cross. In 420, an elaborate cross adorned with gold and precious stones, called the *crux gemmata*, was erected there, the donation of the Emperor Theodosius II. The rock with its cross was a particularly popular artistic motif. According to literary sources, it was surrounded by gold and silver screens, and there were steps leading to its top.

The rock of Golgotha was also traditionally associated with the burial place of Adam and the site of the Sacrifice of Isaac. In the sixth century, people would point out the altar on which Abraham intended to sacrifice Isaac and on which Melchizedek laid his gifts for Abraham. Near the rock, ceremonies were held in connection with the many sacred relics kept in the church: "The bishop's chair is placed on Golgotha behind the Cross (the cross there now), and he takes his seat. A table is placed before him with a cloth on it, the deacons stand round, and there is brought to him a gold and silver box containing the holy Wood of the Cross. It is opened, and the Wood of the Cross and the Title are taken out and placed on the table. As long as the holy Wood is on the table, the bishop sits with his hands resting on either end of it and holds it down, and the deacons round him keep watch over it. They guard it like this . . . Thus all the people go past one by one. They stoop down, touch the holy Wood first with their forehead and then with their eyes, and then kiss it, but no one puts out his hand to touch it. Then they go on to a deacon who stands holding the Ring of Solomon, and the Horn, with which the kings were anointed. These they venerate by kissing them . . . " (*Egeria's Travels*, 37. 1–3).

Opposite:
Column that served as a reliquary from the church at Dor. Above the carved niche, which apparently held a stone, is the following inscription in Greek: "Stone from the holy Golgotha." The niche was presumably covered by a metal cross, which has not survived, but the holes for the nails with which the cross was attached to the column can be clearly seen.

The cross on the hillock of Gologtha, relief on a chancel screen
from the church at Horvat Bata in Carmiel, 6th century CE

The ornamented cross
(*crux gemmata*)
on the hillock of
Gologtha, impression
on the handle of a
pottery vessel,
provenance unknown

The cross on Golgotha,
detail of the decoration
on a lead ampulla
(see p. 200)

On entering the Tomb of the Resurrection she kissed the stone which the angel
removed from the Sepulcher door.

Jerome, on Paula's journey

The Holy Sepulcher

According to the New Testament, after Jesus was taken down from the cross, he was buried by Joseph of Arimathea "in his own new tomb which he had hewn in the rock" (Matthew 27:60). Three hundred years later, Constantine ordered the rock around the tomb to be cut away from its surroundings, converting the cave into a small, independent structure on a level surface. The Emperor then added columns and an entrance with an elaborate roof, and overlaid the tomb with silver and gold. (The Rotunda surrounding the burial cave today appears to have been built after the time of Constantine.)

The tomb building, called the Anastasis ("Resurrection"), appears in various forms in the visual representations of the period. An especially common theme is that of the Two Marys beside the Empty Tomb: "Now after the Sabbath, toward the dawn of the first day of the week . . . Mary Magdalene and the other Mary went to see the sepulcher. And behold, there was a great earthquake; for an angel of the Lord descended from heaven and came and rolled back the stone, and sat upon it. His appearance was like lightning, and his raiment white as snow . . . But the angel said to the women, 'Do not be afraid; for I know that you seek Jesus who was crucified. He is not here, for he has risen . . .'" (Matthew 28:1–6).

The depictions of the tomb are sometimes detailed and sometimes schematic, and the building's appearance is not always consistent. In some cases, the amount of space allotted for the illustration made only a symbolic representation possible. At the same time, it is generally believed that certain lines recurring in many of the depictions attest to the tomb's true form, such as the concentric shape (round or hexagonal?), the surrounding columns, and the entrance with its screens along the sides and in the doors.

The Piacenza pilgrim, who visited the Holy Land in the 560s, describes the decorations on the tomb in the following manner: "There are ornaments in vast numbers, which hang from iron rods: armlets, bracelets, necklaces, rings, tiaras, plaited girdles, belts, emperors' crowns of gold and precious stones, and the insignia of an empress. The Tomb is roofed with a cone which is silver, with added beams of gold" (*Piacenza Pilgrim*, 18).

Opposite: Depictions of the facade of the Holy Sepulcher as it appeared in the 6th century on a bronze censer (below), a bronze ring, and a silver bracelet (see p. 162). The provenances of the objects are unknown, but they are all attributed to the Holy Land.

Facade of the Holy Sepulcher on a lead ampulla (see p. 200)

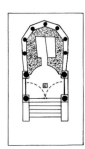

The stages by which the burial cave was made into an independent structure during the time of Constantine

The Holy Sepulcher within the Rotunda as it appeared during the Byzantine period, proposed reconstruction

The Holy Sepulcher in the center of the Rotunda today

Let a church then be thus: with three entries in the type of the Trinity. And let the diakonikon be to the right of the right-hand entry, to the purpose that the Eucharists, or offerings that are offered, may be seen. Let there be a forecourt, with a portico running round, to this diakonikon. And within the forecourt let there be a house for a baptistery . . . Then let there be a throne facing east; to the right and to the left places of the presbyters . . . And let this place of the throne be raised three steps up, for the altar also ought to be there.

Testament of Our Lord, I. 19

Previous page: Marble dedicatory plaque from
the Byzantine period

The Architecture and Liturgy of the Early Church

Michele Piccirillo

The first Christian buildings in Palestine (apart from the second–third-century "congregational house" in Capernaum, known by pilgrims as the "House of St. Peter") date from the first half of the fourth century. They were constructed during the reign of the Emperor Constantine, who permitted the practice of Christianity and ultimately adopted it as the official religion of the Empire. In many cases, these early churches were erected on the initiative of the royal family, Constantine and his mother Helena, to commemorate sites associated with important traditions, such as Jesus' birth in Bethlehem, his teaching and glorification on the Mount of Olives, his tomb in Jerusalem, and God's apparition to Abraham at Mamre, north of Hebron. As Eusebius, bishop of Caesarea and a contemporary of Constantine, explains in the *Life of Constantine* (*Vita Constantini*): "Choosing in that region three sites which had the honor to contain three mystic caves, he [Constantine] honored them with rich constructions. Thus establishing in the grotto of the first manifestation [the Nativity] the veneration which it deserved, honoring on the other hand, on the peak of the Mount of Olives the memory of the last Ascension, exalting at the intermediate grotto [the tomb] the victory with which the Savior crowned all his struggle. The Emperor embellished these sites thus making the sign of salvation shine all over the place."

In the *Ecclesiatical History* (*Historia Ecclesiastica*), Eusebius provides us with descriptions of both the basilica in Jerusalem (also called the Martyrium), built on Constantine's orders to the east of Jesus' sepulcher, and the basilica built in Tyre at about the same period. These first churches, like the contemporaneous church at Antioch and the Church of the Holy Apostles in Constantinople, were structurally so well suited to their liturgical function that the churches built in the following centuries in the region exhibit little innovation, apart from being somewhat reduced in scale. One may assume that such a fixed type had architectural antecedents, as Eusebius himself, in describing the basilica in Tyre, suggests: "But we especially, who had fixed our hope upon the Christ of God, had gladness unspeakable, and a divine joy blossomed in the hearts of us all as we beheld every place, which a short

Reconstruction of the interior of a 6th-century church at Gerasa in Jordan

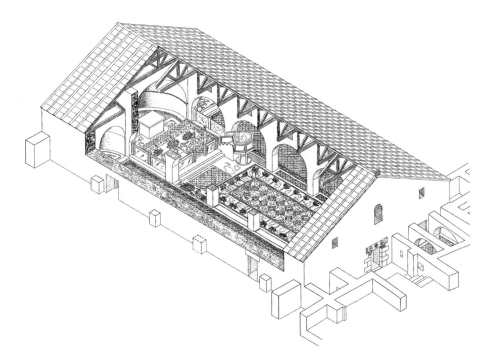

Proposed
reconstruction of
the Church of the
Lions at Umm al-Rasas
(Kastron-Mefaa), Jordan

time before had been laid in ruins by the tyrants' evil deeds, now reviving as if after a long and deadly destruction, and temples [churches] rising once more from their foundations to a boundless height, and receiving in far greater measure the magnificence of those that formerly had been destroyed."

Nearly all the fifth- to sixth-century churches that archaeologists have excavated and continue to excavate in the areas of the Roman-Byzantine provinces of Palestine and Arabia were built, in terms of their basic elements, on the plan of the basilica described by Eusebius. With only a few exceptions, these structures were oriented east, the direction the congregation faced when praying, in symbolic reference to Jesus, *sol oriens ex alto* ("the sun rising from above").

The following remarks are limited, therefore, to the plan of the basilical church. On the basis of its description, we shall also attempt to reconstruct some elements of the liturgy; this is no easy task, as practically none of the liturgical texts of the period that might have assisted us have survived.

Architecture

In Greek inscriptions found in sixth-century churches, the church building has several names, ranging from such generic terms as *oikos* (house), *topos* (place), *domos* (home), and *pedon* (locality) to more specific liturgical terminology, such as *naos* (temple), *ecclesia* (congregation), *martyrion* (martyrial church or chapel), and *eukterion* (oratory).

The basilical church consisted of a large hall ending in an apse on its eastern side. This hall was divided into three sections by columns or pilasters supporting the roof or a gallery. The central section is referred to as the nave, while the sections on the sides, which were normally smaller, are called aisles. The entrance was situated on the western side, opposite the apse. The focal point of

Marble altar from the church of the monastery at Khirbet ed-Deir in the Judean Desert, 6th century. Around the edge of the altar is a dedicatory inscription mentioning the names of the donors: Alaphaeos the deacon and Aias the monk.

the church was the altar, located in front of the apse on a raised area called the *bema* or presbytery, reserved for the officiating clergy and separated from the congregation by a chancel screen.

From the street, one usually entered an atrium (forecourt) surrounded by porticoes, with a fountain or cistern in the center. Occasionally, all that remains of the atrium is the portico adjacent to the church. In many cases, the atrium and the entrance to the church were separated by an additional broad corridor, called the narthex.

The *Bema* (Presbytery) and the Chancel Screen

The *bema* was a raised platform, one or two steps higher than the floor of the church, which in its simplest form was square or rectangular. It was situated in front of the apse and was reserved for those clergymen directly responsible for performing the liturgical rites: the bishop, the priests, and the deacons.

The chancel screen, which surrounded the *bema*, was made of stone or marble slabs either decorated in relief or reticulated. The slabs were held upright by one-meter-high posts with spherical or conical heads. Two pillars, each composed of a square post and a colonnette, two meters high, flanked the entrance to the *bema*. From depictions of buildings in contemporaneous mosaics and frescoes, and from hooks (originally attached to the pillars) that have come to light in excavations, we know that a kind of lintel was added to the capitals of these pillars, and thus, that the entrance to the *bema* was also set off by curtains that hung down from above. At a later stage, in the eighth century, the chancel screen posts were sometimes replaced by tall columns. It is possible that in such cases, the *bema* was enclosed by a particularly high partition that hid the priest and the altar – not unlike the *ikonostasis* found in present-day Orthodox churches. Eusebius, in reference to the church in Tyre, writes: "Finally, he [Paulinus, bishop of Tyre] placed the sanctuary – i.e., the Holy of Holies – in the center and, so that this, too, should be inaccessible to the multitude, he fenced it off with wooden lattices perfectly fashioned with artful workmanship."

The Altar

As mentioned above, the altar, which resembled a table, was situated on the *bema*, usually in the center, on the chord of the apse. It was the core of the church, on which the ceremony of the Eucharist was performed. On it the chalices of wine mixed with water and the platters of bread were placed.

Excavations at various sites have shed light on the altar's development: The oldest evidence points to a portable altar of wood or metal. A sixth-century text entitled a *Short Description of Jerusalem*

(*Breviarius de Hierosolyma*) relates that the altar of the Martyrium in Jerusalem was made of silver and gold and was supported by nine colonnettes. The rhetor Choricius, describing the altar of the Church of St. Sergius in Gaza, writes: "You will see at the same time the Holy Table made of silver based on colonnettes equally precious."

By the sixth century, the altar was already stationary, with the altar slab (*mensa*) supported by four colonnettes embedded in the floor. In most cases, the altar slab was rectangular or in the shape of the letter *sigma* and had lobes carved around its perimeter. In churches where mosaic floors had already been installed, it was necessary to dismantle a section of mosaic before setting the colonnettes in the floor. In certain cases, in order to avoid damaging the mosaic, a long, wide stone slab with sockets for the colonnettes was placed over the mosaic, serving as a base for the altar. Already in the sixth century, however, mosaics were produced that took the altar into account, as can be seen, for example, in the church at Shoham, the Church of St. George on Mount Nebo (586) and the Church of the Lions at Umm al-Rasas (Kastron-Mefaa), southeast of Madaba, dating from the time of Bishop Sergius of Madaba (574–603).

In the eighth century, after the Muslim conquest, the altar bases constructed in the sixth century were rebuilt of stone masonry. The new bases incorporated the colonnettes of the earlier ones, as in the churches at Umm al-Rasas.

In many churches in the region, such as the Church of St. Stephen at Umm al-Rasas and the church at Rehovot-in-the-Negev, the altar was covered by a *ciborium*, a kind of canopy supported by four columns about two meters in height.

Starting in the sixth century, a reliquary – a stone box for sacred relics – was sometimes placed beneath the altar, either within a stone recess or directly on top of the floor. The reliquary resembled a small sarcophagus. Its lid had raised corners (*acroteria*) decorated with crosses carved in relief or separately fashioned from metal. The reliquary was divided into two, three, or four compartments, into which sacred relics, mainly bits of bones belonging to martyrs (sometimes held within smaller boxes made of precious metal), were placed. In the center of the lid was a hole shaped like a funnel. Another hole was in the side of the reliquary; beneath this hole stood a goblet. The worshipers would

Marble slabs and posts from an *ambo* (pulpit), from the Martyr's Church at Tel Iztabba, 6th century

Ambo (pulpit) carved from bituminous stone, from the Church of St. Theodore at Khirbet Beit Sila, north of Jerusalem, 6th century

Proposed
reconstruction of the
church at Horvat
Hesheq, Western
Galilee, 6th century

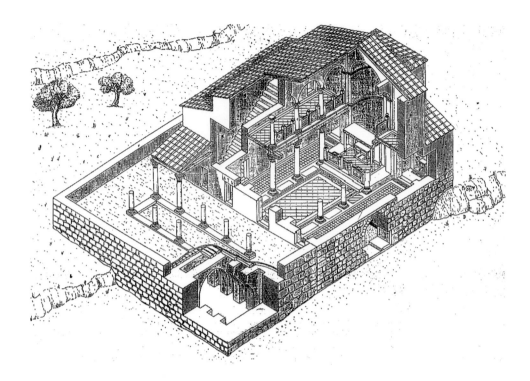

pour various oils into the upper hole and collect them when they flowed out from the side hole,
after they had been sanctified by contact with the holy relics. The oils were regarded as amuletic
(*phylacteria*), capable of protecting those who carried them or the houses in which they were kept.

Offering Table

Next to one of the two western sides of the chancel screen, but still within the area of the *bema*, stood
a table for receiving the donations and offerings of the congregation. One side of this square table,
which was smaller than the altar, rested on two posts embedded in the floor or in a stone base,
while its other side rested on the screen.

Synthronon

Many churches contained a *synthronon*, step-like benches built against the semicircular recess of
the apse on which the priests would sit. An empty space or special seat was usually reserved in the
center for the bishop or for the main officiating priest. Of the Church of St. Sergius in Gaza Choricius
writes: "The center of the wall facing east is hollowed out like a shell, and there it is usual for the
bishop to sit." Along both sides of the *bema* were the benches used by the other clergymen who
took part in the ceremony of the Eucharist. Eusebius describes the seating in the basilica in Tyre:
"When he [Paulinus] had thus completed the church, he adorned it in fitting fashion with lofty thrones
in honor of the bishops and, in addition, with benches ranged in order for the general [clergy]."

Previous pages:
A corner of the
exhibition featuring
a reconstruction of the
bema of a typical church
in the Holy Land

Ambo (Pulpit)

The clergyman responsible for reading the scriptural texts would walk from the *bema* to the *ambo*,
a raised pulpit that stood out prominently in the hall; in the churches of Palestine it was on the

Stone slabs and a post, painted red, from the gallery balustrade of the church at Horvat Hesheq, Western Galilee. Fragments of stone slabs decorated with similar patterns, which were also used as gallery balustrades, have been discovered in several other churches in the Western Galilee. The chancel screens of these churches, however, are all made of marble.

northern side and in the churches of Arabia on the southern side. Excavations have shed light on the historical development of the *ambo*. Like the altar, this structure was originally portable and made of wood. It became stationary only in the second half of the sixth century, when it became monumental. In the Church of the Lions at Umm al-Rasas, it comprised two elements: stone steps and a hexagonal platform supported by four colonnettes on a round stone base. The steps of the *ambo* rested on the steps of the *bema*, and on their sides were two carved slabs, held by two posts, which served as banisters. The last step supported the hexagonal platform, which was surrounded and enclosed by five carved slabs. A similar *ambo* was recently excavated at Khirbet Beit Sila, outside Jerusalem.

Lighting

The church was lit by the row of high windows set in the walls above the columns (clerestory) and by the windows of the facade. In addition to natural light, tall bronze lamps were used, as well as chandeliers (*polycandela*), which hung from the ceiling and between the columns or were placed on stands in the area of the presbytery. Their role, however, was not merely functional; they also symbolized Jesus Christ as the "Light of the World." A similar concept is expressed by a sixth-century pottery lamp, made in the vicinity of Jerusalem, which bears the Greek inscription: "The light of Christ shines for all."

The Service Rooms or Sacristies on the Sides of the Apse

In typical sixth-century churches, two small rectangular service rooms were found on either side of the apse. The entrances to these rooms were from the eastern end of each aisle. Their floors were

Northern church
at Shivta, Negev,
6th century

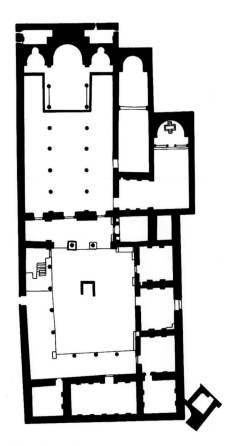

Plan of the northern
church at Shivta

paved with mosaics like the rest of the church, but they were usually about a step higher. Near the back wall, one or two cupboards usually stood. In the fifth-century work, the *Apostolic Constitutions* (*Costituziones Apostolicum*), these rooms are called *pastoforia* (small sanctuaries), a term that does not appear in later texts. In churches with three apses, they were replaced by the two side apses.

Rooms Adjoining the Church: *Diakonikon and Baptisterium*

In many churches, external structures were added on to the main building, next to the northern or southern walls. These extensions held rooms where the baptismal rites were performed, or where the offerings and liturgical objects were stored. They usually had mosaic floors and sometimes also contained an apse, as, for example, in the northern church at Shivta and the church at Beth Yerah. The extension was generally divided by a screen into two separate areas of different floor heights. The eastern area, which was the higher one, sometimes contained an altar. In rooms not divided by a screen, a table rested on the eastern wall.

In the Church of Moses on Mount Nebo, the adjoining northern room, which contained a baptismal font built of stone masonry in the shape of a cross, with a mosaic floor, was called the *diakonikon* (a room for the deacons, the priest's assistants). This name is found in a dedicatory inscription dating from the year 530: "the holy *diakonikon* of God with the holy pool of rebirth." A few decades later, the church was rebuilt, and this room became a long raised chapel, divided into two separate rooms by a step and a screen. In 597, a new baptistery chapel (called in the inscription on its floor *fotisterion* – the place where people are enlightened) was built next to the southern wall. It had an apse separated from the chapel by a screen and a cruciform font carved from a single block of stone. Within a short time, another chapel with an apse, dedicated to the "Mother of God" (*Theotokos*) and containing an altar supported by four small colonnettes was added to the baptistery on its western side. Similarly, in the Propylaea Church at Gerasa, a round room with a mosaic floor, built by doubling an existing Roman *exedra*, can be seen next to the facade. In the inscription on its mosaic floor, it is called the *diakonia*, but no further explanation is provided.

Liturgy

As mentioned above, we unfortunately do not possess any contemporaneous work that would throw light on the liturgy used in a typical sixth-century church, which in the provinces of Palestine would have followed the Jerusalem liturgy and in *Provincia Arabia* that of the Antiochene Patriarchate. A small amount of evidence can be gleaned from works of the previous period (2nd–5th century) and of the succeeding period (7th–10th century). However, all information is largely hypothetical, or based on comparisons with the later liturgy, which was heavily influenced by the liturgy of the Constantinopolitan Patriarchate.

In the Atrium

The atrium was the forecourt, situated between the street and the sacred area of the church, in which the worshipers gathered. Eusebius describes the atrium of the basilica at Tyre as follows: "[Paulinus] did not allow a man who had come inside the gates to proceed straightaway to the inner sanctuary with impure and unwashed feet, and so interposed a large space between the church and the outer entrance. This space he enclosed in the form of a rectangle and adorned all round with four porticoes (*stoai*) placed at right angles to each other and uplifted on all sides by means of columns. The intervals between the columns he closed off with latticed wooden barriers reaching up to an appropriate height, while in the middle he left open to the sight of heaven an atrium (*aithrion*) exposed to the beams of the sun and affording excellent air. Here he placed tokens of the sacred purification by fitting out fountains right opposite the church; these flowed with abundant water and provided cleansing for those proceeding further into the sacred precincts."

Baptismal font hewn in stone from the northern church at Shivta

In the regions that had become Christian, the atrium was still in the sixth century an intermediary space between the street and the church. The inscription above the lintel of the atrium of the Church of St. Theodore at Gerasa contrasts the Christian ceremony with the sacrificial rites which had formerly taken place in the temple of Artemis nearby: "I have been made a wonder and a marvel at once to passersby, for all the cloud of unseemliness is dispelled, and instead of the former eye sore the grace of God surrounds me on every side. And once from the four-footed beasts, that toiling died and were here cast out, spread forth a baleful stench, and often would a man going by grip his nose and stop the passage of breath, shunning the foul odor. But now the

Baptismal font hewn in stone, from the central church at Lower Herodium, 6th century

Marble capital decorated with crosses from Ashdod-Yam

Stone capital decorated with crosses surmounting amphorae, from the church at Mazzuva, Western Galilee

Proposed reconstruction of the Martyr's Church at Tel Iztabba
in northern Beth Shean, 6th century

wayfarers that pass over the scented plain carry their right hand to their brow making the sign of the precious cross."

In the typical sixth-century church, there was a fountain or cistern in the center of the atrium. In certain cases, however, a water vessel or basin made of marble or stone stood next to the entrance to the church hall, within the portico or the narthex. In these instances, the fountain for ablutions in the atrium, under the open sky, as existed, for example, in the Cathedral Church at Gerasa, was replaced by the *colymbion*, that is, a holy water stoup, which then as now served only for the symbolic rite of purification, so that the worshipers would be ready with purified bodies and hearts to attend the liturgy. Eusebius, in his description of the atrium, also addressed a second function: "This is the first halting place for those that enter, affording both beauty and splendor to everyone, and serving as an appropriate station for those who as yet lack the first initiation." In the fourth century, the atrium was the area where the catechumens – candidates for conversion to Christianity through baptism – gathered.

In the Church

Eusebius, in his description of the church at Tyre, writes: "Also contained in this sanctuary are thrones and a multitude of benches, and seats." Within the church, everyone had his or her place: the priesthood – on the *bema*, around the altar; the congregation – in the nave and aisles; and the children – around the chancel screen. Worshipers could also sit on the stone or wooden benches placed along walls in the aisles, where a little light penetrated through openings in the walls.

In *Didascalia Apostolorum* of the third century and the *Testament of Our Lord* (*Testamentum Domini*) of the fifth century, we read that it was the task of the deacons to receive the offerings of the congregation in a service room (*diakonikon*). Arculfus, a seventh-century pilgrim, noticed in Jerusalem a large wooden table between the Anastasis (the domed rotunda built over the tomb of Jesus) and the Martyrium (the adjoining basilica), on which the worshipers put their donations for the poor. Elsewhere, a small table on the *bema*, next to the screen, fulfilled this function.

The Liturgy of the Word (*Parola*)

The first part of this celebration, dedicated to the reading of and commentary on selected scriptural passages, took place on the *ambo*. The persons (lector, deacon, and priest) responsible for the reading and for the sermon mounted the *ambo* and read the passages that had been chosen. Psalms were sung, and then a sermon was delivered by the bishop or priest. This part of the liturgy ended with a "kiss of peace," a condition for participation in the ceremony of the Eucharist, in accordance with Jesus' words: "First be reconciled to your brother, and then come and offer your gift" (Matthew 5:24).

Already in the second century, Justin Martyr of Neapolis (Nablus) wrote: "When the prayers end, each of us gives the other a kiss of peace. Afterwards they bring bread and a cup of wine mixed with water for the person heading the assembly of brothers." The bread and wine were carried in by the deacons,

Stone capital decorated with crosses within *aediculae* (niches), provenance unknown

as expressed in the *Apostolic Constitutions*: "Then the deacons and the lesser priests divide the tasks of supervision and the sacred service next to the altar . . . They bring the breads and the chalices prepared for the holy repast and set them on the altar." In the writings of Pseudo-Dionysius (Dionysius the Areopagite, 6th century), the procedure is described as follows: "After the whole gathering sings the hymn of the Catholic Church, the members of the higher priesthood help the lesser priests to arrange the holy sacrifices, the holy bread, and the cup of benediction on the altar."

The Eucharist

The part of the ceremony that is hardest to reconstruct owing to the absence of contemporary texts is the celebration of the Eucharist, which took place at the altar in the center of the *bema*. On the basis of earlier texts, there is reason to assume that the deacons brought to the altar the chalices with the wine, the water, and the platters of bread – the oblations or *prosfora* (gifts) – for the priest to sanctify with his blessing.

According to the Constantinopolitan liturgy (9th–10th century), the oblations were carried in a procession from the room next to the entrance to the church and placed on the altar. In contemporary Greek Orthodox liturgy, which originated in Constantinople, the preparation of the oblations begins with a ceremony, apparently established only in the fourteenth century, which takes place in the room on the northern side of the apse. The room was therefore called the *protesis* (offering), while the room on the southern side has been called since then the *diakonikon*. Judging from the inscriptions on mosaic floors of sixth-century churches of the Holy Land, these two names are not historically suitable.

At the altar, the priest blessed and sanctified the oblations with a solemn benediction (*anafora*). This was followed by the Holy Communion, in which the oblations were distributed among the members of the congregation, marking the end of the ceremony.

The oblations that had not been consumed by the congregation were carried by the deacons to service rooms near the apse or adjoining the church, where the clergy also left their liturgical

Mosaic inscription with instructions concerning a tomb in the church of the Monastery of Lady Mary, Tel Iztabba, northern Beth Shean, 6th century

vestments. In addition, we may suppose that these rooms, called the *pastoforia*, also had the function, as mentioned in the *Testament of Our Lord*, similar to that of the *diakonikon*, of storing the books of the liturgy, the chalices, the platters, the processional cross, and the reliquaries. The latter were sometimes presented for the adoration of the worshipers before they were put on permanent display beneath the altar or in the *aediculae* (shrines) in the side apses.

Baptism

The act of entering the Christian faith, which was a condition for participation in the celebration of the Eucharist in the church, took place in the "holy pool of rebirth," as it is referred to in the inscription from the *diakonikon* at the Church of Moses on Mount Nebo. The baptismal font was often built as a waterproof masonry pool in the form of a cross, with steps on its side for descending and ascending. Later it was made from a square or circular block of stone, in which a hollow was carved in the shape of a cross.

Normally, the font was located in a chapel known as the *baptisterion* or the *fotisterion*. In the more complex examples, such as that of the basilica of St. Theodore at Gerasa, the baptismal complex consisted of two rooms connected by a corridor, attached to a chapel with an apse on the side of the church. According to archaeologists, the candidate for baptism left his clothes in the southern room and descended into the pool, where the bishop or the priest, assisted by the deacon or deaconess, would baptize him. He would then enter the adjoining room, where he donned a white garment and continued on into the chapel and the church to take part in the liturgical celebration as a full-fledged participant.

Cult of the Martyrs

In sixth-century churches with three apses, the cult of the holy martyrs was celebrated chiefly in the side apses, where the reliquaries were exposed for veneration by the faithful.

In the Church of St. Stephen at Umm al-Rasas, we can trace the different stages of the cult of a martyr's relics in the northern service room at the end of the aisle, which was given special emphasis since the church's construction. At first this was a square room with a screen at the entrance, but an altar with posts, embedded in the mosaic floor, was added later on. In a second stage, an apse was added to the room, which now also had a vaulted ceiling and an arched door. On the wall in the center of the apse an *aedicula* (shrine) was built, dedicated to the cult of St. Stephen, whose remains had been brought from Jerusalem.

Funerary Practices

In the sixth-century church, special persons, priests, or donors were customarily buried in the compound of the sacred edifice – inside the church, in the narthex, or in funerary chapels added to the building. One of the most interesting discoveries was made in the church of the Monastery of Lady Mary at Beth Shean-Scythopolis. There, a Greek inscription indicates how to find and open the *pellaikon* (stone slab) of the tomb hidden beneath the mosaic floor near the chancel screen. "Where the wreathed cross is, [there] lies the lid of the mouth of the tomb, which has rings. Whoever wishes (to bury) shall lift the wreathed cross, and he will find the lid and bury. And if the Lady Mary, who founded this church, should desire in future to lay down (a dead) in this tomb, (she) or anyone of her family at any time, I Elias, by mercy of God a recluse, in the name of the Father, the Son, and the Holy Ghost, curse and anathematize whoever after me hinders her or any of hers, or removes this inscription of mine."

Chancel Screens

The *bema* (presbytery) and the nave were separated by a screen consisting of square posts interspersed with carved panels bearing a variety of motifs. The panels were held in place by grooves that ran along the sides of the posts. Chancel screens are perhaps the most common type of church decoration to have survived from antiquity. Many are made of marble and may even have been imported as finished products, but some, made of local stone, were clearly carved in this region. Occasionally, the motifs appearing on the marble screens are identical to those on screens carved from local stone. The great variety of decorative motifs exhibited by the screens point to the existence of local workshops staffed by expert craftsmen.

All of the chancel screens bear carved frames, usually with classical profiles. As mentioned above, the frames enclose a wide variety of designs, though it is possible to discern a few common patterns that recur with only minor variations. A particularly common motif is the cross-flower within a laurel wreath. The laurel wreath, a symbol of victory in the classical pagan world, is also known in Jewish and Samaritan art. Inside the wreath, between the bars of the cross, are fleurs-de-lis. At the bottom of the wreath are two undulating ribbons terminating in ivy leaves. Occasionally, additional crosses protrude from these leaves. Chancel screens of this type have been discovered at various sites in Israel and Jordan. Similar screens were also used in synagogues of the period; these bear a menorah instead of a cross in the center.

Another group of chancel screens, known in both marble and local stone, bears a motif depicting the cross on the hillock of Golgotha, generally represented by three semicircles. Occasionally, the cross is flanked by a pair of deer, gazelle, or birds. A screen of this type is still in use in the church of St. Catherine's Monastery in Sinai. Birds also decorate screens of local stone bearing foliate scrolls.

Opposite:
Limestone chancel screen decorated with a continuous pattern of vine scrolls, grape clusters, and birds, from the northern church at Nizzana, Negev

Fragment of a marble chancel screen decorated in relief with a flamingo, from the church at Shavei Ziyyon, Western Galilee

Chancel screen of
reddish stone
decorated in relief with
two deer flanking a
cross in the shape
of an amphora,
apparently from the
Hebron hill region or
Judea

Fragment of a marble
chancel screen
decorated in relief with
a deer carrying a
blossom in its mouth,
next to a central cross,
provenance unknown

Fragment of a marble chancel screen decorated in relief with the portrait of a saint, from the church at Nahariyya

Below:
Marble chancel screen decorated in relief with the popular motif of a cross-flower within a wreath flanked by crosses, from Massuot Yizhaq, Northern Negev

Fragment of a marble chancel screen decorated in relief with a ram lowering its head before the hillock of Golgotha, which is surmounted by a cross, from Horvat Karkara, Galilee

Below: Marble chancel screen decorated in relief with a rare motif depicting a lamp (or censer) suspended within an *aedicula* and bearing a Greek inscription: "In the days of Procopius the priest," from the church at Susita, east of the Sea of Galilee

Tables

Many tables – rectangular, round, or horseshoe (*sigma*)-shaped – have come to light in the churches of this region. The tabletops are made of marble, local stone, or bituminous stone, which is easy to carve, and the edges are always raised or surrounded by a wide strip, forming a frame or border. At times, a series of carved lobes, with raised borders, runs along the edge. Tables with incised mythological or hunting scenes along the edge have also been discovered in churches. The legs, made of marble like the tabletops, were carved to resemble miniature columns, complete with bases and capitals. Tables with wooden legs or bases also undoubtedly existed, but none have survived. From indications on stone and mosaic floors, it appears that the table legs were fixed to the floor. Yet no signs have been found on the undersides of the tabletops of any place where the legs could have been attached to the tops, and it is thus difficult to know exactly how the tables stood.

Rectangular limestone lectern, from the church at Horvat Hesheq, Galilee

Opposite:
Above: *Sigma*-shaped table of bituminous stone with carved lobes around the edge, from the central(?) church at Lower Herodium.
Below: *Sigma*-shaped limestone table, with a raised border and a carved cross in the center, from Tel Masos, Eastern Negev.

The function of the various tables is unclear. Since similar tables have also been found in private houses, there seems to be no clear connection between the shapes of the tables and their function. Some tables served as altars, but according to scholars, from the time altars became stationary (that is, from the sixth century), they were generally rectangular. Other tables were used as lecterns, for receiving gifts brought by the faithful, and perhaps as secondary altars in ceremonies related to the cult of the martyrs, which were held in the rooms adjoining the apse. Some of the tables found in monasteries were undoubtedly used for dining.

Like the other marble artifacts discovered in churches, some of the tables were probably produced near the famous marble quarries of the eastern Greek islands and imported, while the ones made of local stone were obviously fashioned here. Certain scholars, however, believe that marble tables were also carved locally by craftsmen from the capital city, Constantinople.

Reliquaries

The collection and veneration of sacred relics formed an important part of the Christian cult in the Holy Land during the Byzantine period. Archaeological remains attest to the fact that by the fifth century, this cult had already become quite extensive. The cult was based on the belief that sacred relics passed their sanctity onto whatever they came into contact with. The relics – bones, bits of clothing, or objects that had belonged to a saint – were kept in special boxes, called reliquaries, and were regarded as amulets or charms that could provide protection and transfer blessings to the faithful. In many churches, reliquaries were the focus of various ceremonies and processions. They also bore important economic significance. Through contact with the sacred remains, secondary relics were produced, which could be transferred from place to place.

The reliquaries were made of marble or stone and sometimes had two or more compartments for storing relics of different types. Excavations have revealed that within the reliquaries, the sacred remains were occasionally kept in smaller boxes made of precious materials. Sometimes, the reliquaries were fitted with metal locks. The lids of the reliquaries usually resemble sarcophagus lids; they have gabled roofs with upturned, horn-like corners (imitating architectural ornaments known as *acroteria*). There was generally a hole in the lid, the rim of which formed a kind of funnel, through which it was possible to insert, by means of a narrow rod, small objects into the box. These objects would "absorb" the blessings of the sacred relics through contact with them. Another means of obtaining the blessing was to pour oil onto the relics through the hole in the lid of the reliquary and to empty it out into the containers that the faithful brought with them for this purpose. Some of the reliquaries have an additional hole at the bottom of the box, to make it easier to remove the sanctified oil. These holes were sometimes equipped with metal spouts.

In most of the churches of this country, reliquaries have been found beneath the main altar, within a depression in the floor. Over time, it became customary to set aside a special place in the church for the cult of the sacred relics – usually the rooms alongside the apse or in the side apses – called *martyria*. The reliquary was kept within a niche in the wall, or on or beneath an altar. This allowed for more convenient and dignified access to the relics. The rooms used for this purpose were either left visible to the congregation or closed by a screen.

Marble reliquary with a flat, sliding lid, decorated with crosses, provenance unknown

Opposite:
Above: Stone reliquary decorated with a cross, with a bronze spout for pouring out the oil, from the church at Horvat Hesheq, Galilee.
Center: Marble reliquary in the shape of a sarcophagus, from the Church of St. Theodore, Khirbet Beit Sila, north of Jerusalem.
Below: Marble reliquary with two compartments, separated by a stone divider, and a lid with a hole for oil, Kfar Rami(?), Galilee.

And to fill the walls ... with all kinds of animal hunts ... fleeing animals, such
as hares, gazelles, and others, while the hunters, eager to capture them, pursue
them with their dogs ...

From a letter by St. Nilus of Sinai

Church Decoration

Early literary sources often refer to the sumptuousness of the church interiors, but very little of this has survived in our region. The only concrete evidence of the spectacular decorations that once graced the walls of the churches of the Holy Land are the colorful mosaic tesserae made of glass and gold glass, excavated among the ruins of many churches. Nevertheless, there can be no doubt that the larger and more important churches were full of wall mosaics and wall paintings, like those visible today in the church of St. Catherine's Monastery, Sinai, and in the churches of Ravenna, Italy.

A few fragments of wall paintings have come to light in this country, for instance, in Rehovot-in-the-Negev and in a chapel in the Mamilla area of Jerusalem. A wall painting depicting saints was recently discovered in a vault within a warehouse complex from the time of Herod the Great. These warehouses were subsequently used for various purposes, and it is not clear what function they served when they were decorated with clearly Christian themes.

Mosaic floors have naturally survived better than wall mosaics, but most are not of a high artistic standard. Because the floors were meant to be walked on, they were not decorated with sacred themes, but rather bore hunting scenes, depictions of everyday life, and representations of plants and animals; only rarely does one come across motifs of symbolic significance. Some of the mosaic floors exhibit the standard Hellenistic-Roman artistic repertoire common in buildings belonging to various faiths. Thus it is not surprising that there is a great resemblance between the floors of synagogues and churches from this period, both in terms of composition and in terms of subject matter (such as the mosaic in the Armenian Chapel near the Damascus Gate, Jerusalem, p. 197, and the floor of the synagogue at Maon Nirim in the Negev).

A large number of inscriptions have been found among the remains of church walls. These are mainly dedicatory inscriptions, which sometimes also bear a decorative pattern. Scriptural verses appear on the walls and on the mosaic floors, as well.

Opposite:
A corner of the exhibition with a mosaic floor depicting hunting scenes and real and imaginary animals, from the northern aisle of the church at Kissufim, Negev. In the center of the aisle was a tomb surrounded by an inscription. An additional inscription (on wall to right) tells of the completion of the mosaic in 578 CE.

Fragmentary marble relief depicting a figure holding a book and making the sign of blessing with his hand. This is a unique find, and it is difficult to determine whether the figure represents a priest, one of the Apostles, or Jesus himself. The object was discovered by chance at Hanita, Western Galilee, and apparently originated in the 6th-century church at the site.

Part of the mosaic pavement from the nave of the church at Khirbet el-Waziya, Galilee. In this section, a camel, a heron, a hare in a basket, and a dog hunting a hare are depicted against a black background.

Gold-glass tile of the 6th–7th century. Fragments of similar tiles have been discovered in Syria and Israel. They were probably inlaid in groups in church walls, producing a dazzling, golden effect.

Portraits of saints painted on glass plaques. The plaques were presumably inlaid in an object of some kind, perhaps a cross. They were discovered in the crypt of the northern church at Rehovot-in-the-Negev.

Saints as orants (worshipers), part of a wall painting from the 6th–7th century, discovered in a vault beneath the governor's palace at Caesarea.

*Everything they use for services at the festival is made of gold and jewels ... They are
beyond description.*

Egeria's Travels, 25.8

The Church Treasure

The most important ceremony in the liturgy was the Eucharist, in which the participants eat a piece
of holy bread and drink wine, as Jesus commanded at the Last Supper. The bread symbolizes Jesus'
flesh and the wine his blood, a reminder of his sacrifice. The ritual objects placed on the altar for
this ceremony were jugs and chalices for the wine and water, a strainer, and patens (platters) for
the holy bread. These implements and the other objects used in the ceremonies – the Holy Scriptures,
processional items, and the sacred vestments – were generally kept in rooms adjoining the church
building.

Opposite:
Jug and chalices of
pottery and glass

The quality of the liturgical vessels of each church reflected the economic situation of the
congregation. The congregants clearly strove to attain the best they could afford, even if these were
pieces made of less precious materials. In northern Syria and eastern Asia Minor, large hoards of
magnificent silver objects have been found, which were donated by the members of the congregations
to the churches. These hoards not only demonstrate the public's devotion to the religious institutions,
but also the availability of silver and the economic prosperity of the period. One can assume that
wealthy churches in this country possessed similar silver implements. The ritual objects of the major
churches of the Holy Land, although none have survived, must have been quite splendid.

Flat silver spoon, with
the name "Petrus"
engraved on the
handle. The place
where the handle is
attached to the bowl
of the spoon is
reinforced with a round
plaque. This method of
reinforcement is typical
of the Byzantine
period; the reinforced
part is usually
decorated.

Apart from ritual objects, the church treasure, like temple
treasures of earlier times, also included money and gifts,
among them objects of great value and even personal jewelry,
received from donations, from the fulfillment of vows, and
from the income from property bequeathed to the church.

The law forbade the sale of this property, except for the purpose of freeing prisoners or redeeming
captives. The contributions of the faithful – members of the congregation and pilgrims – were the
church's main source of revenue and were used for its renovation and adornment.

Part of the mosaic pavement from the church at Kissufim, depicting "Calliora" and "the Lady of Silthous" donating sixteen gold coins and a chicken

Silver chalice and strainer from the "Hama Treasure," northern Syria, mid-6th century

The chalice bears a dedicatory inscription in Greek: "In fulfillment of a vow of Heliodoros and Akakios, children of Thomas, together with (that) of those who belong to them," as well as five official stamps attesting to the quality of the silver. The handle of the strainer is inscribed: "Of St. Sergius."

The names of the donors appearing on the chalice are also found on other vessels, many of which bear the same dedication to St. Sergius. On the basis of the inscriptions, which mention donors from a few families, and the objects' similar style and craftsmanship, scholars have attributed more than fifty silver vessels to a single treasure belonging to a church of St. Sergius in the vicinity of Hama. The objects were apparently produced in Constantinople, having been commissioned by the wealthier members of the local Syrian community, who donated them to the church.

The silver treasures of the Hama region in northern Syria and Sion in Asia Minor contain chalices and patens, as well as ladles, strainers, and spoons. Less common are the silver sheets for covering furniture, fans, elaborate bookbindings, and lamps. The stamps on the objects make it possible to date them fairly accurately.

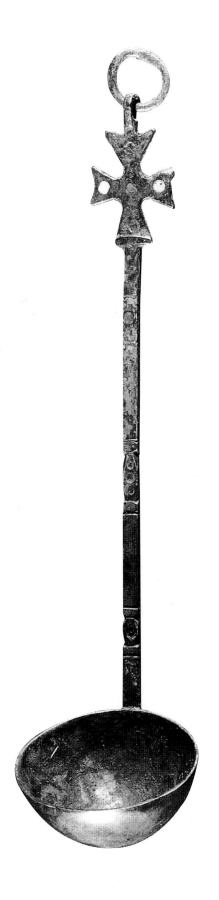

From left to right:
Silver ladle-strainer
with traces of enamel
decoration.
Spoons with crosses at
the ends of the
handles and rings for
suspension.
Spoon decorated with
delicate engraving,
from Caesarea.

Cast bronze processional crosses with engraved decorations, 6th century, provenance unknown

In the cultic processions held at the holy sites and in churches, crosses of different sizes and materials were carried. They were decorated with scenes popular in the minor art of the period (see the cross fragment on p. 154).

The upper bar of the cross to the right shows Jesus holding a book in his left hand and raising his right hand in blessing. The center depicts an orant (worshiper) – apparently Mary – flanked by two angels, one on each side. The lower bar bears a Greek inscription: "For the fulfillment of the vow of Leontius." At the base of the cross is a protrusion, by means of which the cross was affixed to a rod.

The upper bar of the second cross also depicts Jesus holding a book in his left hand and raising his right hand in blessing. The center bears a scene of the Annunciation. On the left is a saint next to a vase with three branches, and on the right a haloed figure swinging a censer. The lower bar portrays a saint on a column. It also bears a Greek inscription: "For the forgiveness of the sins of Leontia." The base of the cross is missing.

Glass chalice with engraved decoration, depicting, on one side, a cross within a building flanked by two angels in profile and on the other, an ornamented cross between two saints. The foot of the chalice has not survived. The chalice dates from the 6th century; its provenance is unknown. A similar chalice depicting two sheep flanking a cross was excavated at Gerasa.

Ivory plaque depicting two angels in flight holding a wreath with a cross in the center, provenance unknown. This is the classical composition used for images of Nike, the winged goddess of victory. Such compositions were easily transformed into Christian scenes.

Ivory pyxis with scenes from the life of Jesus, provenance unknown

In the scene of the Nativity (left), the cradle rests on a kind of stone altar. This was the standard composition for such scenes, which may reflect the depiction of the Nativity in the Church of the Nativity in Bethlehem. The cradle is flanked by an ox and an ass, which were added to the scene on the basis of Isaiah 1:3: "An ox knows its owner, an ass its master's crib," believed to refer to the birth of Jesus. Next to the cradle stands the midwife Salome, mentioned in the Apocryphal New Testament, whose hand withered when she questioned the divinity of the infant. The use of her hand was only restored after she touched him. The scene has an exact parallel on the lower part of the ivory plaque featured on the next page. The pyxis also depicts the Annunciation and the Journey of Mary and Joseph to Bethlehem (right). Such objects may have served as reliquaries.

Carved ivory hand found in the church at Dor, 5th–6th century. On one of the fingers a ring is visible. This unique find may have served as a bishop's scepter. Similar, but larger, bronze hands bearing crosses on globes have been attributed to this region.

Ivory plaque depicting the Adoration of the Magi, provenance unknown

In the scene, Mary and Jesus are portrayed frontally, while the three wise men stand beside them, wearing oriental garb and pointed caps and bearing gifts. For the sake of symmetry, the figure of an angel was added. The bottom of the plaque depicts the Nativity.

In the Roman period, the decoration of furnishings and other objects with carved ivory plaques was one of the means by which rulers expressed their wealth and status. The use of carved ivory continued into Christian art. Here, too, ivory plaques – which were obviously not large – were inlaid one next to the other in furniture and decorative objects. A common scheme used for ivory inlays, which may have served as bookbindings, consists of several plaques joined together: in the center, a large picture of, for example, Jesus and Mary; above, a scene depicting a pair of angels (opposite page); on the sides and below, additional small plaques.

Gold necklace (opposite) and coins and a bracelet (left), from the treasury of the Monastery of Lady Mary, Beth Shean

In excavations at Beth Shean conducted in the 1930s, a 6th-century monastery with a church and adjoining rooms was discovered near the city's northern wall. The rooms of the monastery were paved with detailed mosaics, one of which mentions the name of the donor, "Lady Mary, Founder of the Church" (see p. 66). In one of the adjoining rooms, which opened on to the church, a hoard was discovered, containing jewelry, gold coins, a bronze censer, and other bronze objects. Presumably, this was where the church treasure was kept.

The coins are of the emperors Tiberius, Mauritius, Phocas, Heraclius, and Heraclius and his son, Heraclius-Constantine. They date from the late 6th – early 7th century.

Bread Stamps

Bread has always had symbolic significance. It has been offered to gods, served to important guests, and used to signify covenants of peace. The practice of stamping dough with special bread stamps before baking it was customary even before the advent of Christianity, though not necessarily for religious reasons. However, when the bread used for the Eucharist began to be stamped, the stamps acquired a distinctively Christian character. At first, the sacred loaves were provided as offerings by the members of the congregation. The deacon would make a note of the gifts and select the loaf to be blessed and used in the ceremony. Over the course of time, a distinction began to be made between the bread used for the Eucharist and other loaves that had been blessed, which were also stamped before being distributed to congregants and pilgrims. These loaves were believed capable of imparting a blessing (*eulogia*) to the faithful.

Various kinds of bread stamps have been found, some of them more ancient than others. It is sometimes difficult to distinguish between them, partly because some types were produced and used over a long period of time. The pottery stamps are particularly large, suitable for stamping whole loaves. Their entire surface is covered with patterns that facilitated the breaking of the bread into small pieces. Other stamps, presumably used for "*eulogia* cakes," bear inscriptions, and their patterns are clearly not meant for making it easier to cut the bread. The most common type is a small stone stamp divided into four sections by a cross and inscribed with letters.

Opposite:
Above: Pottery and stone bread stamps bearing names, crosses, and letters – acronyms of the phrases "Jesus Christ who conquers evil" or "Jesus Christ son of God," A and ω (the first and last letters of the Greek alphabet), and so forth.
Below: Large pottery and stone bread stamps found mainly in northern Israel, 6th century and later.

Pottery bread stamps bearing benedictory inscriptions, 6th century

After these three psalms and prayers they take censers into the cave of the Anastasis, so that the whole Anastasis basilica is filled with the smell.

Egeria's Travels, 24. 10

Censers

The burning of incense played an important role in early Christian ritual, and many censers have come to light in excavations. The censers were suspended throughout the church and swung during ceremonies, which fanned the coals and caused the scent of incense to permeate the hall. Depictions of a man holding a censer can be seen on various objects of the period, for example, on processional crosses, and on *eulogia* tokens from Syria with the figure of St. Simeon Stylites on a column.

Most of the censers are made of cast bronze in the shape of a rounded or ribbed bowl. Around the rim are three hooks, loops, or holes, so that the censer could be suspended from a chain. The majority of the censers also have bases or legs. Another type, with a perforated lid, has a tall, wide base and was presumably not meant to be carried around the hall. A large group of bronze censers is characterized by crowded decorations depicting scenes from the life of Jesus. The scenes, which are schematically designed, are difficult to decipher; the details were incised after the vessels were cast. A few examples of this type were used in churches and monasteries of the Middle East until fairly recently. Some bear incised dedicatory inscriptions – in Coptic, Syriac, Arabic, and Armenian – added at a later stage (the Armenian inscription is dated 1649). Scholars have found it difficult to determine when these censers were produced. The decorations are essentially Byzantine, and there are examples on which the figures seem to have been defaced, presumably in the time of the iconoclasts. At the same time, the inscriptions indicate that the censers continued to be used – and were perhaps even manufactured – over a very long period of time. The prevailing view today is that this group of censers was produced at the beginning of the Islamic period.

Pottery censer, 6th–7th century

Opposite: Bronze censer-bowl from Jericho, suspended from a chain decorated with crosses

Bronze censers decorated with scenes from the life of Jesus

Bronze censer on a high pedestal, with an openwork lid and a clasp

Bronze censer in the
shape of a head

Opposite:
Bronze censers from
Jerusalem, Beth Shean,
Shoham, and Yatir

Great glass lanterns are burning everywhere . . . in front of the Anastasis, and also
before and behind the Cross.

Egeria's Travels, 24.7

Lighting and Suspended Ornaments

Finds from excavations have confirmed the literary descriptions and visual representations, which show that churches were lit by a variety of means. The natural light that penetrated the church through the high clerestory windows and the windows of the facade was clearly insufficient, and in any case, since liturgical rites were also held in the evening, additional lighting was necessary. In most ancient churches, fragments of glass oil lamps were found, as well as the remains of the devices used to suspend them. Sometimes, the oil lamps were placed in bronze chandeliers, which held several lamps. Glass bowls decorated with engraved patterns were also occasionally added to these chandeliers; the patterns were visible when they were illuminated from behind.

Opposite:
Crosses and ornaments in the shape of Christograms from churches in the Western Galilee: Nahariyya, Shavei Ziyyon, Evron, and Khirbet el-Waziya

A particularly complex type of chandelier, very few of which have survived, resembles a metal drum, the rim of which has holes for branches that held glass oil lamps. Such chandeliers were heavily ornamented and were undoubtedly found in only the wealthiest churches.

In the churches of the Western Galilee, particularly the church at Nahariyya, long bronze chains, to which crosses and various ornaments were attached, were suspended from the ceiling beams. Among the ornaments are bronze strips joined together in the shape of the Christogram I, X and surmounted by an arch. This ornament has not been found anywhere else. The church at Nahariyya was destroyed in a fire. Its metal ornaments were found scattered on the floor in a manner that made it possible to restore them.

Engraved glass bowl, apparently used to decorate the center of a chandelier, from Bezet, Western Galilee

Glass oil lamps with wick holders
suspended by bronze hanging devices

Bronze lampstands and oil lamps.
The oil lamps are decorated with crosses.

Opposite:
Bronze chandelier,
designed to hold seven
glass oil lamps,
provenance unknown.
The chandelier has a
cross in the center.

Left: The chandelier
with seven glass oil
lamps from Dor.
(Only the stems of the
lamps have survived in
all but one.)

ΥΠΕΡΠΛΑΤΩΕΝΑΓΟΤC
ΑΝΑΤΟΛΥΟΥΜΕΝΟCΟΤΑ
ΒΟΗΘΟΥΠΡΕCΒ5ΜΕΝΟC
ωΤΔΡΕΟΥΑ ΓΝΔ ΤΤ ΕΤΟΥC
ΦΛΔ

Church Functionaries

The main functionaries of the Church were the bishops, the priests, and the deacons; there were also various kinds of attendants. One could be appointed priest from the age of thirty, and deacon from the age of twenty-five. At the head of the large churches was a bishop (*episcopos*), who was assisted by a council of elders (*presbyters*). The deacons helped the bishop with the collection and distribution of charity and with the ceremonial duties. As a rule, appointments were made by the bishop, but some of the officer-holders were chosen by the congregation, subject to the approval of the other Church officials.

The lives of those who served the Church were governed by ecclesiastical law. It was the Church that decided where each one would serve, and it was forbidden to take a position elsewhere except on orders from above. The different functionaries came from various professional backgrounds and sometimes, they continued to practice their former occupations while in service, though they could not engage in moneylending or in the management of property, and they were forbidden to hold public office.

Imperial law exempted members of the priesthood from paying taxes and from public service, and they were judged in separate law courts belonging to the religious establishment. Their salaries were paid directly from the bishopric's property. In the East, married individuals were not excluded from serving in the Church, but those already ordained were not allowed to wed. Women served in the office of deaconess.

Opposite:
Marble tombstone with a Greek inscription: "Came to rest Stephen (son) of Boethos, priest, now resting with the saints, on the 1st of the month Audynaios, indiction 13, year 534." The year 534 of the *Provincia Arabia* era corresponds to 639 CE.

Ostracon from Shivta:
"To Father Johannes, son of
Bictor, Lector, greeting. You have
completed one (unit of) work in
this cistern." The inhabitants of
the Negev towns were required
to perform compulsory
maintenance work on the local
cisterns. This ostracon attests to
the fulfillment of this duty by a
lector (one of the lowest ranking
positions in the Church) named
Johannes.

Mosaic inscription in Greek from
the Armenian monastery north
of the Damascus Gate,
Jerusalem, late 6th – early 7th
century: "In the days of Silvanus,
the god-beloved deacon and
abbot, the present [mosaic inlay]
was done and the apse and
annex of the church, of . . .
[cubits length] and of six cubits
height. Remember me O Lord in
Thy Kingdom."

Greek epitaph on a limestone slab: "Here rests the servant and bride of Christ, Sophia the deaconess, a second Phoebe, who fell asleep in peace on the 21st (day) of the month of March of the 11th indiction, year 319. Lord God ..."
The slab was found in the 19th century in secondary use in a building on the Mount of Olives.

III

Having been persuaded, he [Mark], all alone and in secret, made the cross at night out of silver and gold, and so it happened that when the cross was finished and raised up, there appeared on it three images designated by names written in the Hebrew tongue, namely on the top arm "Emmanuel," and on the lateral arms "Michael" and "Gabriel."

Martyrion of St. Procopius

In the diakonikon were kept some pieces of the venerable wood of the all-holy Cross ... The hegumen Stephen put some of those pieces in a cross of solid gold set with precious stones that was made by his order for the monastery.

Cyril of Scythopolis, *Life of Euthymius*

Previous page: Section of the mosaic floor from the
church at Horvat Beer Shema, Western Negev

Christian Images and Symbols

Yael Israeli

Beliefs and ideas have always been expressed by means of signs and symbols, images and pictures. The period under discussion – the fourth to the seventh century – is no exception, and thus the various visual expressions produced at this time can teach us much about life and beliefs during the time of the spread of Chrisitianity.

The artistic idiom dominant in the Mediterranean countries during Christianity's formative years was that of the classical world, in its Hellenistic or Roman cast, though it differed slightly in each country, owing to the fusion of Hellenism with local traditions. Byzantine art, at least at the outset, continued to employ this accepted language of imagery, which now served an entirely different ideology: Art in the Christian world was enlisted as a means of disseminating the new religion and inculcating its concepts and values.

From a stylistic standpoint, this was a period of transition from naturalistic to symbolic art and from three-dimensionality to two-dimensionality. The new symbolic language combined artistic traditions from the Ancient Near East with features from the common artistic vocabulary. Scenes from the classical repertoire along with biblical themes from contemporary Jewish art were used by artists to create new pictorial forms that carried religious messages. Some of the images remained true to their sources, and it was their symbolic interpretation gave them Christian content. In other cases, the old images were used to create new, Christian scenes. The change was not immediate, but occurred in waves: at times the new spirit predominated, and at times it waned. In fact, themes and images from the classical repertoire persisted throughout the first centuries of the Byzantine period, until the Islamic conquest of the Middle East.

At the same time, opposition to pictorial representation was also voiced. In a letter to Constantine's sister, who had requested a portrait of Jesus, Eusebius, bishop of Caesarea, asked: "Who, then, would be able to represent by means of dead colors and inanimate delineations the glistening, flashing radiance of such dignity and glory?"

Double-sided pendant made of two pieces of gold leaf decorated by repoussé. One side depicts Jesus with his arms about the shoulders of a couple holding hands. This was the standard formula for depicting marriage in Roman art, but in this case, the traditional Roman figure of Harmony is replaced by Jesus. The figures are surrounded by the inscription:"My peace I give to you" (John 14:27). The other side of the pendant depicts the Annunciation.

In the Byzantine period, there was an increased use of wall decorations – both paintings and mosaics – which replaced the sculptures and reliefs that characterized Hellenistic-Roman art. Locally, however, very little of these sumptuous decorations has survived, and only a few examples have been preserved in Greece and Italy. In St. Catherine's Monastery in Sinai, built by the Emperor Justinian in the sixth century, a wall mosaic has been preserved in the apse. This mosaic, which was probably executed by expert craftsmen from the capital Constantinople, is the only concrete testimony to the use of this type of decoration in our region. However, convincing evidence of the existence of wall mosaics and paintings is found in a literary source – Choricius's description of the churches in Gaza – although the churches themselves have not survived.

Choricius describes the central apse of the Church of St. Sergius, built by Stephen, governor of Palestine, and Marianus, bishop of Gaza, at the beginning of the sixth century, as follows: "The latter is adorned with gilded and silver mosaic, and displays in the center the Mother of the Savior holding on her bosom her new-born Son; on either side stands a pious band . . ." Later on, he discusses more than twenty scenes from the life of Jesus that graced the church walls.

Unlike the wall mosaics, which have not survived, many mosaic floors have been preserved both in synagogues and in churches, and there is a striking resemblance between them. Besides the mosaic carpets containing geometric and floral patterns, landscapes, and hunting scenes with realistic and mythical animals – all characteristic of the Hellenistic tradition – there are also depictions of biblical stories, especially those relating miraculous deliverances, such as the Sacrifice of Isaac and Daniel in the Lions' Den. The story of the Angels' Visit to Abraham and Sarah at Mamre and the Sacrifice of Isaac were popular among Christians in the Byzantine period because they were interpreted as prefigurations of events in the life of Jesus.

In addition to depictions of biblical stories, one should also mention the motifs derived from classical imagery and the Ancient Near Eastern repertoire, which reappear in Byzantine art and which, though they are not specifically Christian, were given Christian significance. Examples include the figures of the Good Shepherd and of Orpheus playing the lyre, as well as the motif of "Mother and Child," which was interpreted as referring to Mary and Jesus. In contrast, pictorial schemes for scenes with clear Christian content eventually developed, as did a standard cycle of images illustrating events from the lives of Jesus and Mary.

Scholars have frequently addressed the question of whether the representations on the small, simple objects that have survived provide an indication of the large pictures on the walls of the sacred monuments in the Holy Land. In the images known to us from vessels and *eulogia* objects, it is possible to discern fixed formulas for the depiction of certain subjects, such as the Two Women beside Jesus' Empty Tomb (cf. p. 44) and the Adoration of the Magi. It could be, however, that that these subjects were simply popular on objects created for pilgrims because of their connection with the holy places – the Church of the Holy Sepulcher in Jerusalem and the Church of the Nativity in Bethlehem – and that they do not throw any light on the nature of the wall decorations. Nevertheless, it is reasonable to assume that at least some of these scenes, as small and schematic as they may be, represent miniature versions of the wall decorations and provide a hint of the splendor that has been lost.

Another uniquely Christian medium that emerged in this period is the icon – a painted wooden panel, usually bearing a portrait of a saint. Icons, which were hung on the walls of churches but were removable, frequently became objects of ritual adoration. In the eighth century, they aroused the ire of the iconoclasts, who called for their destruction. For that reason, only a few examples from the period preceding the eighth century have survived (most of them in St. Catherine's Monastery in Sinai).

The spread of Hellenistic culture and the syncretism of the Roman period, which carried over into the early Byzantine period, resulted in the creation of new religious streams and in the fusion of motifs and formulas from different cultures and languages. Identical objects for daily use were produced by the same craftsmen for customers of different religions, who did not find the decorative patterns on the objects offensive and may have even read their own meanings into them.

The amulets common in the Holy Land in this period combine pagan formulas and magical elements from many different faiths, and in the fourth to the sixth century, they were used by people of various religions. The forms, signs, and symbols of supernatural power, which were used as means of protection even before the advent of Christianity, were joined by biblical verses and divine names to produce magical formulas, regarded as capable of protecting believers and preserving them from harm.

Octagonal gold wedding rings. Above: Jesus is shown standing between the wedded couple. Below: Jesus and Mary can be seen blessing the couple. Beneath them is the Greek inscription: "Harmony." The band is decorated with almost the complete cycle of scenes from the life of Jesus: The Annunciation, the Visitation, the Nativity, the Baptism, the Adoration of the Magi, the Crucifixion, and the Two Women beside the Tomb.

Early Symbols: the Christogram and the Fish

One of the early symbols of Christianity was the Christogram – a monogram based on letters from Jesus' name and epithets in Greek. In the fourth century, this symbol was more common than the cross, which only became widespread in the fifth century. The Christogram symbolized the triumph of Jesus and sometimes Jesus himself, and it was believed to have protective power. According to Eusebius, the Christogram first appeared to Constantine in a dream, after which he decided to place it on his military standard. Assisted by this emblem, Constantine proceeded to win battle after battle, until he became Emperor of the Roman Empire, the first to rule in the name of Christianity.

There are various types of Christograms: One combines the first letter of the name Jesus in Greek (I) with the first letter of the word Christ – meaning Messiah – in Greek (X). Another is based on the first two letters of the Greek word for Christ (XP). A third consists of the letter P with the addition of the horizontal bar of the cross. (This bar is sometimes also added to the first two types).

Another early symbol was the fish. The letters of the Greek word for "fish": IXΘΥς, also form the initials of the phrase, "Jesus Christ, Son of God, the Savior." The fish motif, which was common in landscapes and fishing scenes in Hellenistic art, acquired Christian significance already in the second and third centuries. The stories of the Miracle of the Loaves and the Fishes (Matthew 14:17–21) and the Miracle of the Draft of Fishes (Luke 5:1–11; John 21:1–14), as well as, perhaps, Jesus' statement about the Apostles being "catching men" (Luke 5:10), enhanced the power of the fish as a Christian symbol. The fish could thus be interpreted as a Christian symbol even in contexts that originally bore no connection to Christianity.

Opposite:
Fragment of a lead coffin decorated with a Christogram, 4th century

Oil lamp of the "Beit Natif" type decorated with a Christogram, 4th century

Oil lamps decorated with Christograms, 4th century.
Left and center: Oil lamps typical of the North African pottery industry.
Right: Oil lamp found in a shipwreck off the coast of Dor.

Pottery bowls with stamped motifs in the center – one a fish and the other a Christogram, 4th–5th century

Fish-shaped mirror-plaque for protection against the Evil Eye, found in a tomb at Dikhrin, 5th century

Elaborate oil lamp in the shape of a fish, with a stamped Christogram on one side and a cross on the other, 5th century

Corinthian capital decorated with fish and a Christogram, 5th–6th century

Part of a mosaic floor depicting a cross, fish, and pomegranates, from the 5th-century church at Shavei Ziyyon

The Cross

The cross was a recognized sign hundreds of years before the time of Jesus, not only in the cultures of this region. After Jesus' crucifixion, however, it became the major symbol of Christian faith and the emblem of Christian salvation. The cross takes various forms. The most characteristic are the cross with bars of equal length and the cross whose lower bar is longer than the three others. Beginning in the Middle Ages, the former came to be known as a Greek cross, and the second, a Latin cross.

The cross is sometimes regarded as the Tree of Life, a particularly common motif in the art of the Ancient Near East. Like the Tree of Life, its form lends itself to symmetrical design, and it is thus frequently depicted flanked by sheep, deer, birds, and so on. In Byzantine art, the cross is often surrounded by a wreath or a circle, with dots or sprouted stalks between its bars.

The cross was the main Christian symbol of identity, and it is frequently found on tombstones and coffins. It also often appears on weights of the Byzantine period, as an official mark of reliability, and on most coins of the Byzantine emperors. In fact, the cross was depicted on a wide variety of everyday objects: it was stamped on eating utensils, carved or painted on the facades of private and public buildings, and erected in fields or along roadsides, as a means of driving off Satan and the forces of evil. Crosses were common on oil lamps, presumably to symbolize the banishment of darkness, and were widely used in jewelry worn by the living and deposited in the tombs of the deceased. Here, the cross had two functions: to adorn and to protect from evil. Crosses were also incised or painted on amulets and placed at the beginning and end of written documents.

The cross served as a decorative motif on mosaic floors, but out of respect for the symbol, this practice was forbidden by an edict of the Emperor Theodosius II in 427: "We decree specifically that no one shall be permitted to carve or to paint the sign of Christ the Savior upon the floor or the pavement or on the marble slabs placed on the ground." Nevertheless, crosses appear on the mosaic floors of churches as late as the sixth century.

Ampulla decorated with a cross and two birds, 6th century

Opposite:
Stone slab from Nizzana decorated with a cross and bearing the inscription: "Christ wins, Christ reigns. Stephen (son) of Patricius made (this) in the month of Loos, in the 10th year of the indiction, (year) 472. May the envious burst!" Year 472 of the *Provincia Arabia* era corresponds to 577 CE.

Part of the mosaic floor of the church at Hazor-Ashdod depicting the ornamented cross and two birds

Fragment of a marble chancel screen(?) from Jericho, decorated with a cross inside a circle and a bird

Left: 4th-century oil lamp.
Right: Oil lamp from Beth Shean, 5th century.
Each of the lamps is decorated with a cross.

Mosaic panel depicting two lions(?) flanking a cross, from the church at Ozem in the southern coastal region

Marble chancel screen from the church of the Monastery of Lady Mary, Tel Iztabba, northern Beth Shean

Stone slab decorated with numerous crosses, from Amra, Negev

Stone lintel from the southern church at Shivta, apparently from the 6th century. The lintel is decorated with a cross, grape clusters, and birds (defaced) and bears the inscription: "Built by Aed the priest in the year 31(?)."

Oil lamps decorated with crosses, most of the 5th–7th century. The lamp on the top right is from the Early Islamic period, but the fact that it is decorated with numerous crosses indicates that it was made for Christian customers.

Oil lamp decorated with a cross, from the 4th century. This is one of the earliest types of lamps to feature a cross.

Zoomorphic vessels with crosses of the Byzantine period

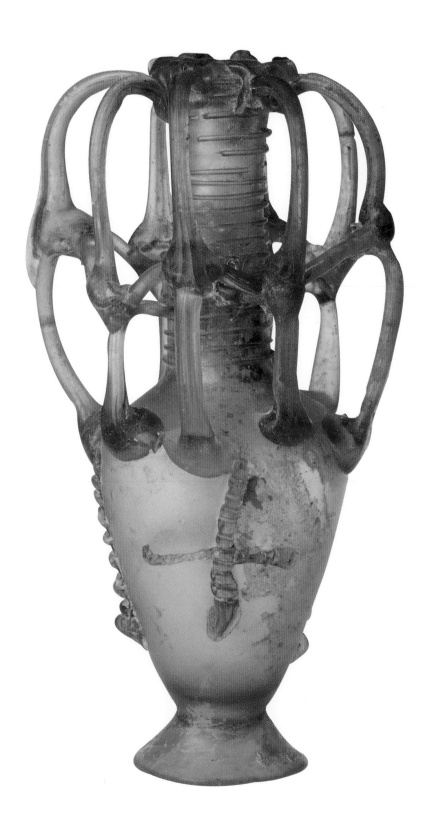

Glass vessel
decorated with crosses,
5th–6th century

Mold-blown glass jugs bearing alternate motifs of crosses and lozenges, which may have been used for oil from the holy sites, Jerusalem(?), late 6th – early 7th century. Apparently, the images all represent the cross on Gologtha: a cross on a double circle, symbolizing the center of the universe, which according to Christian faith was situated at Golgotha; a cross with branches growing from its base, alluding to the Tree of Life in the Church of the Holy Sepulcher, which was likened to the Garden of Eden; and a cross on steps (a semi-realistic depiction).

Left: Glass bottle
decorated with crosses,
5th–6th century.
Right: Glass oil lamp
decorated with crosses,
5th–6th century.

Plaster plaques decorated with crosses, birds, and human torsos. The holes in the center originally held mirrors, which were used to avert the Evil Eye.

Above: Metal doorknobs
Below: Bronze inlays

Opposite:
Hoard of 50 gold coins found in an oil lamp at Horvat Qav, near Carmiel. The hoard was probably hidden prior to the destruction of the farmhouse in which it was found. Most of the coins belong to the emperors Phocas, Heraclius, and Constans II. The latest one, from 663, tells us when the hoard was hidden.

Right: Lead seals from Beth Shean and Ziqim, Negev

Various bronze weights from Beth Shean and Nizzana. The weights of the Byzantine period almost always bore crosses as a mark of quality. Sometimes, the cross is depicted inside an *aedicula* (shrine).

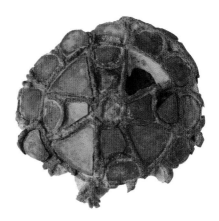

Opposite:
Cross-pendants from Jerusalem. In the course of excavations of a burial chapel in the Mamilla district of Jerusalem, three crosses (two in center and one below) were found, representing the types used in this region during the Byzantine period. In addition, a cross consisting of wood set in a bronze frame (above) was discovered in the vicinity of the shops near the Jaffa Gate. This was probably "wood from the True Cross," thought to provide a particularly sacred blessing.

Left: Gold and bronze brooches with glass inlays in the shape of a cross. The bronze brooch was found in the northern church at Nizzana.

Left: Stone crosses. The fragmentary cross was excavated at Horvat Hur, near Tel Shoqet. Right: Gold cross decorated with birds, inlaid with blue glass.

Small cross-shaped
bronze pendants
decorated with circles
were the most popular
type of amulet in the
Holy Land during the
Byzantine period. Most
have been discovered
in tombs.

Cross jewelry of various types, made of lead, glass, silver, and gold.

Tombstone from the northern church at Nizzana. The epitaph reads: "Came to rest the blessed Stephen son of Obathos on the 5th of the month of Dios, in the 9th year of the indiction, year 500." The year 500 according to the *Provincia Arabia* era corresponds to 605 CE.

A child's(?) lead coffin decorated with crosses from Beit Safafa, Jerusalem. Lead coffins were popular in this region during the 3rd and 4th centuries. Similar coffins bearing Jewish symbols were found in the Jewish cemetery at Beth Shearim.

Tombstones from Haluza decorated with crosses. One is engraved with the first letters of the Greek alphabet.

Tombstone from Rehovot-in-the-Negev with the name "Aaona" in Greek.

I am the good shepherd. The good shepherd lays down his life for his sheep.

John 10:11

The Good Shepherd

A traditional metaphor for God or a leader guiding his community can be found in the image of the shepherd leading his flock, as in Psalms 23:1 "The Lord is my shepherd, I shall not want." In the catacombs of Rome, depictions of Jesus as the Good Shepherd are quite common. This image, based on Jesus' words concerning the shepherd who has lost one of his flock – "and when he has found it, he lays it on his shoulders" (Luke 15:5) – was one of Christianity's earliest visual motifs. Jesus is generally depicted as a young man bearing a lamb or kid on his shoulders, echoing pagan sculptures of the Greek god Hermes carrying a ewe. Although in comparison with Hellenistic-Roman art, sculpture is rare in early Christian art, sculptures of the Good Shepherd are relatively numerous.

Other depictions of Jesus as a shepherd with his sheep are based on the figure of Orpheus, who is usually shown wearing a typical shepherd's costume and a Phrygian cap, sitting among the beasts and enchanting them with his music.

Opposite:
Marble statue of the Good Shepherd from the vicinity of Gaza, 4th–5th century. The back is not carved, and thus the statue may have been one of a group or part of a piece of furniture.

And [Mary] took the purple and sat down upon her seat and drew out the thread.
And behold an angel of the Lord stood before her ...

Book of James 11:1–2

The Annunciation

The Annunciation is the name given to scenes depicting the appearance of the angel Gabriel before Mary, in order to inform her that she is about to give birth to a son: "And behold, you will conceive in your womb and bear a son, and you shall call his name Jesus" (Luke 1:31).

Several versions of the scene are known. In many cases, the interpretation is based on the Apocryphal New Testament (specifically, the work known as the Book of James, or the Protoevangelium). Mary is shown seated in a high-backed chair spinning threads for a curtain, while the angel stands in front of her holding a staff. The picture is sometimes accompanied by the inscription, "Hail, O favored one, the Lord is with you" (Luke 1:28).

Most of the items bearing scenes of the Annunciation were probably sanctified objects used by pilgrims. However, a few large, colorful representations of the scene have also survived, such the icons in St. Catherine's Monastery in Sinai and textiles from Egypt. It has been proposed that the *eulogia* flasks and tokens decorated with this scene were produced in Nazareth and acquired there by pilgrims.

Silver token depicting the Annunciation, excavated at Caesarea. Despite its small size, the scene is clear. The other side of the token is engraved with an image of the Sacred Horseman.

Opposite:
Above: Copper plaque depicting the Annunciation. The surrounding inscription reads: "Blessing of the Holy Mary ..." The end of the inscription is missing.
Center: Piece of jewelry made of two attached gold leaves, decorated in the center with scenes done in the repoussé technique. One side depicts the Annunciation and the other the Baptism. On the side of the chair and between the two figures is the beginning of the verse: "Hail, O favored one." Plaques such as these served as the centerpieces of necklaces worn by men and women alike. They originated on the eastern Mediterranean littoral, but in most instances, the precise provenance is difficult to ascertain.
Below: Depiction of the Annunciation on a pottery ampulla (see. p. 201). Surrounding the scene, within a frame, is the above-mentioned verse in its entirety. It is possible that the flask held oil or water from the site of the Annunciation in Nazareth.

Mother and Child

The subject of fertility and motherhood has always been a source of fascination, and depictions of mother and child are known from many places and periods.

As is the case with the Good Shepherd motif, it is often difficult to determine whether a specific depiction of a mother and child has Christian significance: in other words, whether it actually represents Mary and Jesus. It may be assumed that figures like the one found at Beth Shean were intended for customers of various religions, who could interpret the images as they pleased.

The figure of the goddess Isis nursing her son Horus was very common in ancient Egypt. In the Roman period, Isis' cult spread way beyond the borders of Egypt, even reaching Rome. Influenced by these widespread images, similar depictions of Mary nursing Jesus began to be produced. Nevertheless, the more common composition in Christian art shows the Virgin seated on a chair with the infant in her arms, both of them wearing halos and looking straight ahead, as is exemplified by the ivory plaque illustrated on p. 93.

Opposite:
Left: Figurine of a woman holding an infant, Byzantine period, provenance unknown.
Right: Figurine of a woman nursing an infant, from Beth Shean, 5th century.

Mary and the infant Jesus on a silver bracelet. The surrounding inscription reads: "Mother of God, help Anna, by your mercy" (see p. 163).

Opposite:
Funerary stele depicting a young mother and her child, engraved and painted on limestone, from Medinet el-Fayum, Egypt, 4th–5th century. Owing to the crosses engraved on the tombstone, this image was believed to be an early depiction of Mary and Jesus. However, the discovery of an inscription indicated that this was a private tombstone: "…twenty-one years old. No one is immortal. Be happy. Courage." It is thus unclear whether the crosses were engraved when the tombstone was first produced, or whether they were added at a later stage, thus lending Christian significance to the scene.

Top row:
Center: Lead plaque with a relief of Mary and Jesus flanked by angels, probably from Syria.
Right: Pottery token depicting Mary and Jesus.

Bottom row:
Left: Pottery stamp depicting Mary and Jesus with two angels, from Deir Dusawi, east of Gaza, 6th century. The infant Jesus holds a book with a cross on the cover. Surrounding the scene is a Greek inscription, part of which is missing: "Blessing of Our Lady, Mother of God, Mary." This object was used for stamping bread or tokens.
Center: Modern impression produced by the stamp.

Behold, wise men from the East came to Jerusalem, saying, "Where is he who has been born king of the Jews? For we have seen his star in the East, and have come to worship him."

Matthew 2:1–2

The Adoration of the Magi

The Adoration of the Magi – the wise men from the East who came to see the infant Jesus, "King of the Jews" – is one of the common themes in the cycle of scenes from the life of Jesus. In the fourth century, this scene was particularly widespread in Italy, especially on carved marble sarcophagi, perhaps because of its suitability to long, narrow surfaces.

The event is depicted in several different ways. In some cases, Mary is seated in the center with the infant on her knees, while worshipers bearing gifts stand on either side of her (as, for instance, on ivory plaques; see p. 93). Mary is always larger than the other figures, and in the interests of symmetry, an angel is sometimes added on one of the sides, or, occasionally, only two gift bearers are depicted. The wise men's costumes and pointed hats reveal their eastern origins; their hands are covered by cloths, and they carry dishes containing the gifts (gold, myrrh, and frankincense). However, in most of the examples that have come down to us – all on small objects of the sixth century – the picture is more schematic and suggestive. Mary is shown from the side, seated in a high-backed chair, and in front of her the three worshipers stand next to each other in a crowded formation. They are depicted with their knees slightly bent as though bowing, and they wear pointed Phrygian caps. Above Jesus' head, a star can be seen.

It may be that this standard image, seen on articles from the Holy Land, indicates that there was once a large picture with this composition in the Church of the Nativity in Bethlehem. In a petitionary letter ascribed to a conference held in Jerusalem in 836 and supposedly addressed to the Emperor Theophilus, it is mentioned that on the facade of the church there was a large mosaic (or painting) depicting the wise men bringing gifts to Jesus and Mary. The wise men were apparently portrayed in Persian garb, and that is why the Persians refrained from destroying the church when the Persian army reached Bethlehem in 614.

Opposite:
The Adoration of the Magi in the center of a processional cross

Brass vessel with a
depiction of the
Adoration of the Magi
and a rare scene of the
Magi before King
Herod, 7th century

Eulogia tokens with depictions of the Adoration of the Magi

The Sacred Horseman

The image of the Sacred Horseman, the deliverer from evil, was one of the most common protective symbols in this region during the Byzantine period. It appears on various types of accessories and jewelry, which served as amulets. The horseman is portrayed wearing a halo and piercing a female demon (who lies at the feet of his horse) or a serpent with his lance. An early example of this motif, depicted on gems, apparently of the third century, is identified by the name "Solomon" in Greek. The motif was especially common in the Byzantine period on engraved bronze amulet-pendants. On such objects, the Greek inscription surrounding the scene is usually: "One God who conquers evil." The other side bears engraved motifs, particularly, the eye motif (the Evil Eye) or the snake, which, like the female figure lying at the feet of the horse, symbolize the forces of evil; the Hebrew phrase "Lord of Hosts" in Greek transliteration, sometimes accompanied by the names of angels, such as Michael or Uriel, also appears. On some of the pendants, the lance terminates in a cross, and there are also examples to which specifically Christian scenes or inscriptions were added. On rare occasions, the horseman is identified by name: St. Sisinnius or even St. George, the martyr whose name is associated with the town of Lod and whose image as a horseman and dragon-slayer is familiar to this day.

These amulets are a fascinating example of the syncretistic trend dominant in the first centuries of the Common Era, when ideas and concepts originating in distant cultures interfused and were accepted by people of different faiths. The figure of the horseman was a symbol used by people of many religions, including Christianity. When it was adopted by Christianity, the top of the lance was given the form of a cross, and the scene became widely used in combination with specifically Christian images on bracelets and other accessories.

Opposite and below: The Sacred Horseman on a steatite mold used for casting metal tokens. The end of the lance is in the shape of a cross. The second scene portrays Mary and the infant Jesus, with an angel opposite them.

Depiction of the
Sacred Horseman on a
bracelet from
Caesarea.
The other side bears
the customary
Samaritan formula:
"There is no God like
Jeshurun."
The Samaritans
scrupulously observed
the biblical proscription
against making graven
images, and thus their
amulets usually bear
inscriptions only. The
formula may have been
engraved on the back
of the bracelet to
impart additional
magical potency.

Above: Bronze amulets depicting the Sacred Horseman, from a burial cave at Gush Halav, Galilee.

Below: Bronze rings with depictions of the Sacred Horseman, from a tomb near Mishmar Haemeq and from Caesarea.

Holy, holy, holy is the Lord of Hosts.

Isaiah 6:3

Words of Salvation

Letters, words, and formulas have captivated people since the invention of writing. Specific words and phrases have been regarded as having beneficial qualities, and the letters of the alphabet, even when not combined to form words but simply written out in order, were believed to possess protective powers. The belief in the power of the written word finds expression in the fixed formulas of blessings, requests, and pleas for help that accompanied gifts to religious institutions, objects of magical significance, and everyday articles. Most of the pleas for assistance are directed toward a specific saint. Like the visual images, the inscriptions shed light on the different sources from which Christianity drew its inspiration.

The letters A and ω, the first and last letters of the Greek alphabet, sometimes appear next to the cross or the Christogram – a monogram based on the name Jesus and his epithets. The source of this combination is Jesus' declaration: "I am the Alpha and the Omega, the beginning and the end" (Revelation 21:6).

Biblical verses interpreted by Christians as prefigurations of the life of Jesus were also quoted in various contexts. The initial verses of Psalm 91 (Psalm 90 in the Septuagint), which speaks of salvation, were especially widespread: "O you who dwell in the shelter of the Most High and abide in the protection of Shaddai . . . He will save you from the fowler's trap . . ." The biblical formula "Holy, holy, holy" was also commonly found in Greek on amulets, and it even had a special name: the *trisagion*.

The use of formulas and words with protective power, such as the "Health" or the phrase "One God who conquers evil," continued even after the Roman period. A common phenomenon found on amulets is the use of letters resembling Aramaic script, but which do not form actual words; it is impossible to know whether they represent a corruption of a particular formula ("Lord of Hosts," for example) or whether they are simply supposed to be ancient letters and do not refer to a specific text.

Opposite:
Above: Bronze bracelet decorated with scenes of the Women beside the Empty Tomb; the Sacred Horseman; the beginning of the first verse of Psalm 91; the Adoration of the Magi. Below: Silver bracelet decorated with scenes of the Women beside the Empty Tomb; Mary and Jesus with the formula: "Mother of God, save Anna"; the Sacred Horseman with the inscription: "Health"; and the inscription: "Holy, Holy, Holy is the Lord." The bracelet band is inscribed with the first verse of Psalm 91.

Part of a mosaic floor
from the church at
Hazor-Ashdod bearing
a decorated cross in a
circle. Between the
bars of the cross are
the letters: I, X (Jesus
Christ) and A, ω
(*alpha* and *omega*,
the first and last letters
of the Greek alphabet).

Stone amulet bearing a depiction of the Raising of Lazarus and the inscription: "Save"; the other side bears the inscription "Uriel, save" and letters in Aramaic script that do not form words.

Left: Metal pendant bearing the first letters of Psalm 91. The other side has a depiction of the Sacred Horseman.
Right: Limonite amulet with an identical motif.

Left: Oil lamp bearing inscriptions in two circles: "Blessing of the Mother of God," "Inscription of Johannes."
Right: Oil lamp bearing the Greek inscription: "The light of Christ shines beautifully for all." Lamps with this inscription were very common, even though the wording is often corrupt. This, however, was apparently not important; it was the intention that mattered.

IV

At that time, before so many monasteries were founded in
the southern desert, the place was lonely and not situated
on a thoroughfare; now on the contrary it is on a pathway,
since all the desert has been colonized by the spiritual seed
of Euthymius.

Cyril of Scythopolis, *Life of Euthymius*

For the blessed Sabas maintained that as the flower precedes
the growth of the fruit, so the cenobitic [communal] life must
precede the solitary life.

Cyril of Scythopolis, *Life of Sabas*

Monasticism in the Holy Land

Yael Israeli

In the early centuries of Christianity, monasticism was a phenomenon of great social, cultural, and economic importance. Its main emphases were prayer, devotion to the Holy Scriptures, and love of God and one's neighbor, values that were realized within a lifestyle of seclusion, frugality, and abstinence.

Monasticism began in third-century Egypt, when a number of pious Christians, wishing to find seclusion and concentrate on the spiritual aspects of religion, retired to the desert. They were rapidly joined by many others, some of whom had fled from persecution or hardships of other kinds. Eventually, communities formed around leaders and exceptional personalities, who arose from the midst of these individuals. The communities comprised dozens and even hundreds of monks, but there were also hermits who lived alone. Over the course of time, these communities took on a definite form, and rules were established to regulate their way of life. Fixed prayers, manual labor, and obedience to superiors were among the salient features of the monastic lifestyle.

From Egypt, monasticism spread to Palestine and Syria. The monasticism of the Holy Land was generally of the moderate kind found in Egypt and Asia Minor, in contrast to the monasticism of Syria and Mesopotamia, which was distinguished by its severe asceticism. In these countries, the monks and hermits were particularly strict in their practices and invented various means of self-mortification, as if competing for the amount of affliction and discomfort they were able to bear.

In Asia Minor, the accepted form of monasticism as decreed by St. Basil was found in settled areas rather than in distant and isolated places. The monks lived together in small communities and devoted themselves to prayer, crafts, and various charitable enterprises, such as helping the sick, caring for orphans, and maintaining hospices for pilgrims and the homeless.

St. Catherine's
Monastery in Sinai

In the sixth century, during the time of Justinian, laws were enacted governing relations between the monasteries and the ecclesiastical establishment. These laws addressed the organizational structure of the monasteries, the acceptance of new members, discipline and conduct, ascetic practices, and the rights and authority of monasteries in matters of inheritance and property. In all cases, the monks were under the jurisdiction of the regional bishop (*episcopos*), and his permission was also required for founding new monasteries. Each monastery was led by a *hegumenos*, who was responsible for the monastery's property and for maintaining discipline. The *hegumenos* was chosen by the monks of his community, but his appointment had to be confirmed by the bishop. In the larger monasteries, there were also priests whose task was to perform the religious rites, as the monks were not necessarily priests themselves.

The major manifestation of monastic life in the Holy Land was the monasticism of the Judean Desert, the "Desert of the Holy City," in which the monks found the space necessary for seclusion and meditation, a link with the great figures of the Bible and of the beginnings of Christianity, and, at the same time, proximity to Jerusalem. Our knowledge of monasticism in this country during the Byzantine period is largely derived from the literature of the period, which has survived in its original language – Greek – or in translations. This literature includes collections of prayers and edicts as well as compilations of stories and legends and biographies of renowned monks. Particularly noteworthy in this context is Cyril of Scythopolis (Beth Shean), who in the mid-sixth century wrote the biographies of seven important monks, among them Euthymius and Sabas.

The lifestyles of the Judean Desert monks took two different forms: Some monks lived in a closed communal monastery – a *coenobium* – where they ate and prayed together. Most of them had separate cells, although some lived in communal rooms. Another type of monastery was the laura, in which the monks lived far apart from one another, each one isolated in his own cave or cell. It was only on Sabbaths and Sundays that they came together for common prayer and a festive meal at the laura's center, where the church was situated. There were also hermits who did not live in any framework. In the more populated areas, most of the monasteries were of the communal variety.

The monasteries generally came into being in the following manner: A monk who sought seclusion in the desert was joined by other monks until a community was formed, and a monastery was built for this community with the help of

Church of the monastery of Kursi, east of the Sea of Galilee

donations. Some of the monks, wishing to isolate themselves once more, left and found a place further away in which to settle. Chariton, regarded as the founder of Judean Desert monasticism, established the first monasteries in the first half of the fourth century, all three of them lauras: Pharan in the Wadi Qelt, Douka on the cliffs of Mt. Quruntul, overlooking Jericho, and Souka (the monastery of Chariton) in a deep ravine northeast of Tekoa. At the beginning of the fifth century, Euthymius founded the first *coenobium*. In the second half of that century, a monk called Theodosius established the largest *coenobium* in the Judean Desert, east of Bethlehem, and Gerasimus established a laura to the east of Jericho, even stipulating the rules that would govern the monks' way of life, their work, and their diet. Around the same time, Sabas, the most famous of the Judean Desert monks, also reached the area. Sabas lived for many years in the desert, was a leader and model for the monks in the region, and founded many monasteries, the best-known being the monastery of Mar Saba, formerly known as the "Great Laura." By the sixth century, dozens of monasteries had been established in the Judean Desert, and the "Desert of the Holy City" came to resemble a settled area on the outskirts of Jerusalem. Roads and paths were laid to facilitate movement, and the monasteries provided accommodation for the many travelers and pilgrims who had come to immerse themselves in the Jordan or to seek out the holy men of the desert.

Bronze oil lamp and stand found in a church, perhaps part of a monastery, at Khirbet el-Shubeika, Western Galilee. The lamp bears a dedicatory inscription mentioning St. Sabas.

The monasteries were built next to springs of water or were equipped with large cisterns. In the *coenobia*, the monastery complex included a refectory, a kitchen, a bakery, and other facilities. Towers were built for defense against desert tribes and bandits. The caves in the cliffs around the monasteries were utilized as living quarters for monks, but larger caves were also adapted for use as churches. Construction was financed by donations, funds from the Christian establishment in Jerusalem, and inheritances received by the monks, many of whom came from well-to-do, educated families outside the country. Literary sources indicate that, apart from praying, the monks also engaged in various crafts, such as basketry, and in the *coenobia*, they performed the basic tasks required to run the institution. Where possible, the monks also tended vegetable gardens and sold what they could not consume themselves. In addition, the monks' duties included serving in the monastery churches. Among the monks' few possessions were copies of the Holy Scriptures, which were very costly and certainly not within everyone's reach. In some of the monasteries, there was a scriptorium where books were copied. Monks in the *coenobia* also trained candidates for the monkhood, in order to prepare them for the monastic lifestyle before they were allowed to live in the seclusion of a laura.

The monks who passed away were buried at the monasteries with which they had been affiliated. In the monastery of Euthymius, the tomb of Euthymius, the monastery's founder, was discovered. Sabas, who died in 532, was buried in the courtyard of the monastery of Mar Saba. In the thirteenth century, his bones were taken to Venice, and only in 1965 were they returned to their original location.

A hermit's cell in Wadi Qelt, the Judean Desert, near the monastery of St. George

In the fourth and fifth centuries, monasteries were established in most parts of the country. The first monasteries in the area of Gaza were founded by Hilarion in the fourth century. According to literary evidence, there were many monasteries in the area of Beth Guvrin (Eleutheropolis), and a few have been discovered in excavations at Beth Shean. In the agricultural areas of the Western Galilee there were monasteries which operated as farms, whose members worked the land and produced olive oil and wine. In the towns of the Negev, most of the churches discovered in excavations were associated with monasteries.

A large concentration of important, wealthy monasteries existed in Jerusalem and Bethlehem. A few of them were built on the Mount of Olives and Mount Zion, and there were some within the city itself. Near the gate of the city's northern wall, the Empress Eudocia founded the monastery of St. Stephen. Cyril of Scythopolis relates that the patriarch Elias built a monastery next to the episcopal palace in Jerusalem and gathered around him those serving in the Church of the Resurrection (the Church of the Holy Sepulcher), who had previously been spread out in the area of the Tower of David. Sabas also acquired rooms for monks in this area and built a hospice of the Great Laura there.

"Private tomb of Sa(muel) Bishop of the Georgians and of the monastery which they bought (or frequented) in the Tower of David," inscription discovered in a cemetery not far from the Tower of David, Jerusalem

Many of the monasteries were built by wealthy pilgrims from the West who settled in the Holy Land. Among the founders of monasteries were also female pilgrims, who established monasteries for women. St. Jerome, the renowned Church Father, arrived in Bethlehem at the end of the fourth century. He came with Paula, a wealthy member of the Roman aristocracy, who had studied under him in Rome together with two of her daughters and a group of pious women. Paula founded a women's monastery in Bethlehem, as well as an additional monastery for men. After her death, her daughter headed the women's monastery.

The monasteries in the settled areas and large towns were more open than the others and maintained ties with the surrounding communities. Their members provided various services, such as maintaining the holy places, officiating at the ceremonies held there, and serving as guides for pilgrims. The hospices for pilgrims were also often within the precincts of the urban monasteries and under their control. In the monastery of Theodosius near Bethlehem, there were three hospices and three hospitals – for visiting monks, for pilgrims, and for the poor – as well as homes for aged monks and for those who had lost their sanity.

The monastic movement spread and gained influence largely through the efforts of a few of its outstanding leaders, who managed to attain positions of authority within the local Church hierarchy and at the holy places. Many of the monks of the Judean Desert were appointed patriarchs and

Monastery of
St. George in Wadi
Qelt, the Judean
Desert

bishops, and quite a few played an active role in the fractious theological disputes of the period. The monastic community in this country was by no means uniform in character: just as the monks came different countries of origin, so were they diverse in their styles and outlooks.

Another region that attracted monks and hermits, owing to the splendor of its desert landscape and its aura of holiness, was the southern Sinai Peninsula. The monks identified the lofty mountain of Jebel Mussa as Mount Sinai, sometimes simply calling it the "holy mountain," and pointed out other landmarks associated with the Israelites' wanderings in the desert: the site of the episode of the Golden Calf, the place where Moses broke the Tablets of the Law, and the site of the Burning Bush, where St. Catherine's Monastery was built. The monastery itself was constructed in the sixth century, perhaps around an already existing church, by Justinian, in response to a request by the monks of the region for protection against the Saracens – nomadic tribes who engaged in robbery and who were particularly active in desert regions and on the outskirts of settled areas. The monastery was thus designed as a fortress, the walls of which remain an impressive sight to this day. The Emperor also provided troops to defend the fortress and sent in Slavic workers, believed to be the ancestors of the Jebeliyeh tribe, who still serve in this capacity today. In spite of the many additions and repairs that have been made over the years, exquisite works from the time of the monastery's original construction have survived. The wall mosaics (see p. 32) and woodcarvings were undoubtedly executed by craftsmen dispatched by the Emperor from the capital city, Constantinople. Owing to the monastery's isolation, early Christian works of art have been preserved there of a kind that has not survived anywhere else. Of particular importance is the collection of early icons, which were not damaged by the iconoclastic movement that caused the destruction of nearly all works of art containing human or animal images in the eighth and ninth centuries.

The decline of the monasteries was gradual. It began after the Muslim conquest, when the link with the center in Constantinople was severed, the flow of pilgrims ceased, and the sources of economic assistance to religious institutions dried up. Few monasteries continued to exist after the first millennium. Even in Jerusalem, only a small number of monasteries have operated without interruption from the Byzantine period until the present.

Of all the monasteries of the Judean Desert, the only one to have been inhabited continuously until the present is the monastery of Mar Saba; in Sinai, St. Catherine's Monastery still operates today.

The Monastery of Martyrius

One of the large, relatively well-preserved monasteries east of Jerusalem is the monastery of Martyrius (Khirbet el-Murassas) at Maale Adumim. Built on a hilltop, it covers an area of ten thousand square meters, has an almost perfectly square plan, and is surrounded by a wall. The monastery was named after its founder – Martyrius – a monk from Asia Minor, who according to Cyril of Scythopolis reached the Judean Desert from a monastery in Egypt. After living for a while at the monastery of Euthymius, Martyrius built a "very famous monastery" nearby. Years later, he was appointed Patriarch of Jerusalem.

Opposite:
Tombstone of
"Paul, priest and
archimandrite," head of
the monastery of
Martyrius, late 5th or
early 6th century

The entrance to the monastery complex was through a gate on the eastern side, next to which stood the main church. In the center of the complex was a spacious courtyard, and around it were living quarters and a bathhouse, as well as large, paved stables with built-in troughs. Outside the wall but close to it was a hospice for pilgrims, which also had living quarters and stables. In the courtyard, next to the church, was the tomb of Paul, one of the heads of the monastery, who is also mentioned by Cyril of Scythopolis. In the northern part of the complex was a cave where Martyrius apparently lived before the monastery was built, and which was later used for burial.

The refectory was a large hall in monastery's northwestern corner, with two rows of columns and benches built along the walls. Next to it was the kitchen, with a second story above and a roomy cellar below. The more important rooms in the monastery were paved with fine mosaics. That of the refectory is especially beautiful and well preserved. A sophisticated drainage system carried the rainwater from the courtyards and roofs to large cisterns.

Excavations have shown that the monastery was built in three stages: The original nucleus of the building was apparently constructed under Martyrius in the fifth century; most parts of the main monastery were built in the sixth century; and finally, the hospice and the refectory were added on later in the sixth century. The monastery seems to have been abandoned during the Persian conquest and was never occupied again.

The monastery of
Martyrius at Maale
Adumim

The monastery of
Martyrius, proposed
reconstruction

Dining utensils found in the refectory of the monastery of Martyrius

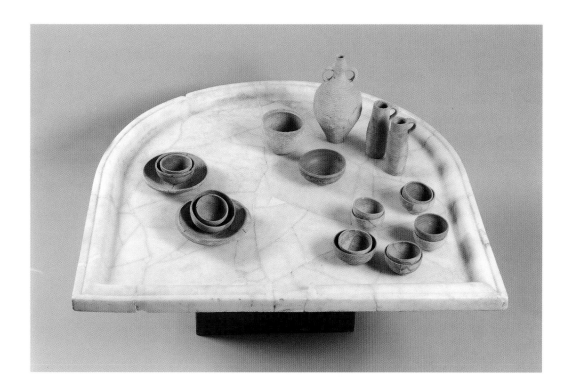

Tables and dining utensils from the monastery of Martyrius

Documentary Evidence from the Monasteries

Most of the monasteries and churches were neglected and abandoned during the Islamic period, and those that continued to exist declined due to a lack of resources and support from the authorities. As a result, hardly any texts or written documents, of which there were presumably very many, especially in the larger monasteries, have survived. Nevertheless, in two places in the country, at Nizzana in the Negev and at the monastery of Castellion in the Judean Desert, numerous documents have been unearthed.

In the excavations at Nizzana, remains have been found of a fortress, a monastery, and two churches that were abandoned in the early Islamic period. Noteworthy among the many finds is a large group of papyrus documents that had been stored in the two churches. Dating from the late sixth and the seventh centuries and written mainly in Greek, with a few in Arabic, the documents have revealed much about economic life in the towns of the Negev. One of the most fascinating documents is a letter from 684 CE – the beginning of the Islamic period – in which the governor of the province, Abu Rashid, asks the governor of Nizzana, George, to provide the bearer of the letter with "a guide to the Holy Mountain" – that is, Mount Sinai. Nizzana was the last stop on the journey from the north to St. Catherine's Monastery, and the starting point of the journey to Sinai. There are also documents that deal with donations to the monastery and church. One of them is a long list of contributions "for special purposes" to "the monastery of St. Sergius" and "the feasts of St. Sergius."

In the monastery of Castellion (el-Mird) in the Judean Desert, another collection of documents was found. Dating from the sixth to the eighth century, these documents include passages from the New Testament and from other religious literature. Most are in Arabic, with a smaller number in Greek and a few in the Christo-Palestinian Syriac dialect used in addition to Greek in the Holy Land during the Byzantine period. These are the first documents in this dialect to have been found in excavations, and they form an addition to the documents in this idiom that exist outside the country.

Opposite: Parchment folio from *Acts of the Apostles* in Christo-Palestinian Syriac, found at the monastery of Castellion. The fragment is from chapter 10, which tells of Peter's visit to the home of the Roman centurion Cornelius in Caesarea. Verses 32–36 on one side and 36–41 on the other are almost perfectly preserved. The folio is dated to the 6th century.

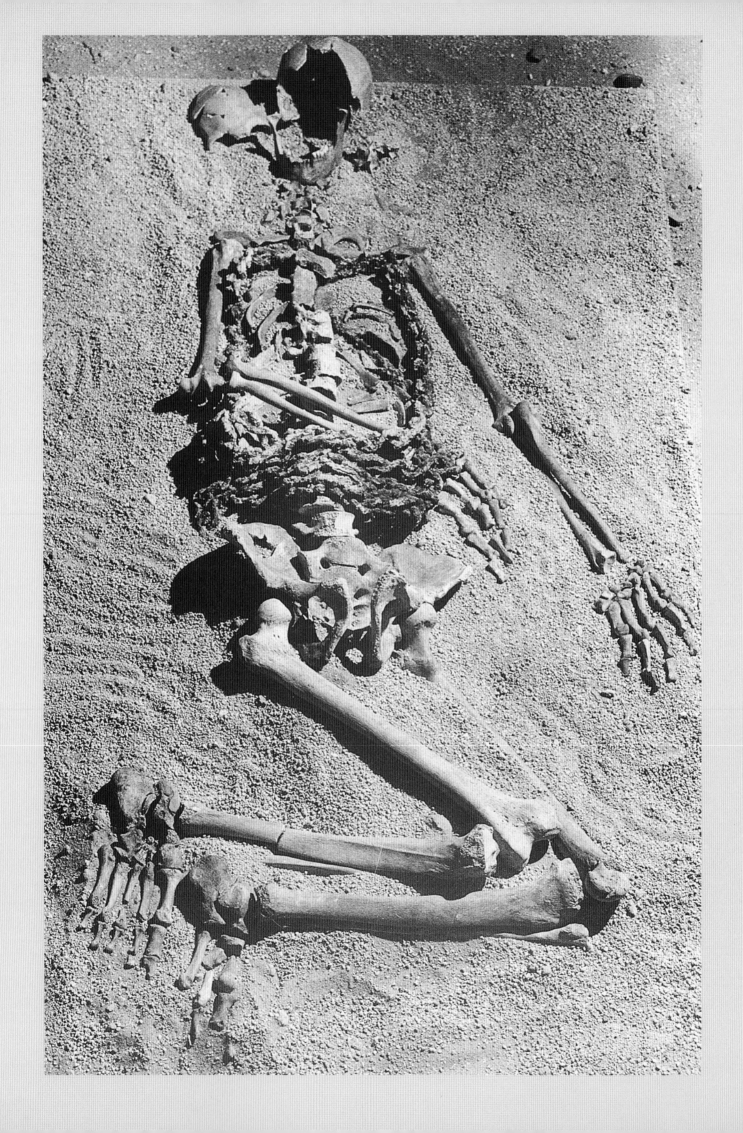

[The women] carried an iron weight that even a man in full strength would not have been able to lift . . . They put an iron collar around their necks, a girdle around their loins, and accessories around their arms and legs.

Theodoret of Cyrrhus, *A History of the Monks of Syria*

The Monk in Chains

The skeleton of a young man whose upper body was wrapped in iron chains was discovered in a cave south of Jerusalem, about five hundred meters northwest of the Mar Elias Monastery. The man-made cave, hollowed out beneath the ground, was reached by a brief flight of steps. The entrance, through a tight, window-like opening, led to a small cell with niches in its walls. From there one proceeded to a slightly larger cell, which was 1.75 meters long, 0.85 meters wide, and 1.70 meters high. The cell was the abode of a solitary monk, whose body remained there after his death.

Opposite:
The skeleton in chains
upon discovery

The walls of the cave were partially covered with stones and the ceiling was constructed as a vault. The niches in the walls were lined with stone and served as cupboards for food and personal belongings. In one of the niches, a small pottery goblet was found, and in the ceiling of another there was an iron hook, from which a metal wire that held a glass oil lamp was suspended. Fragments of the lamp that hung in this simple device were found on the floor beneath the niche. An iron knife, two horseshoe-shaped pieces – perhaps from the man's sandals – a belt buckle, and a few pottery sherds were also discovered in the cell. Apparently, this was the sum total of the monk's worldly goods.

The custom of wrapping one's body in chains was a well-known method of self-mortification, particularly in Syria. The chains found on the skeleton are six meters long and weigh approximately six kilograms. They were wrapped in such a way that they could be removed, and thus it is clear that the monk did not wear the chains against his will.

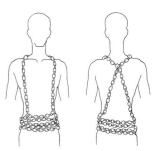

Reconstruction of
the way the chains
were worn

At a later stage, a round tower was erected above the subterranean structure. The builders were clearly aware of the existence of the cave and did not block its entrance. In the opinion of the excavators, the tower was built as a memorial to the monk who lived and died in the cell below.

V

*From Sion we went to the basilica of Saint Mary, with its
great congregation of monks, and its guest houses for men
and women. In catering for travelers they have a vast number
of tables, and more than three thousand beds for the sick.*

Piacenza Pilgrim (Antoninus), 23

*It is three staging-posts from Jerusalem to Elusa, and seven
from Elusa to Aila ... It is eight staging posts from Aila to
Mount Sinai, if you chose the short way across the desert,
but twenty-five if you go through Egypt.*

Theodosius, *Topography of the Holy Land*, 27

Pilgrimage to the Holy Places

Yael Israeli

The Church of the Holy Sepulcher in Jerusalem, built on the orders of Constantine, Emperor of Byzantium, was publicly dedicated on the 14th of September 335. The festivities were attended by pilgrims from many different lands, who came to Jerusalem to visit the holy places. Constantine's building activities in Jerusalem and Bethlehem represented the beginning of the institutionalization of the veneration of holy places, a process that would determine the character of the Holy Land in the Byzantine period, reaching its climax in the sixth century. Pilgrimage to the holy places was, in fact, the most dominant manifestation of early Christianity in the Holy Land. With the encouragement of the Byzantine emperors, construction in the country soared, and the waves of pilgrims brought abundance and economic prosperity to the land. Many of the pilgrims ultimately settled in the country, altering its social fabric and creating an almost cosmopolitan atmosphere. After the Muslim conquest of the region in 632, however, all these phenomena began to decline, until they almost entirely disappeared.

Even before the adoption of Christianity as the official religion of the Roman Empire, pilgrims visited the Holy Land. Nevertheless, Helena, Constantine's mother, who arrived in Jerusalem in 326, is regarded as the first pilgrim, and from the time of Constantine onward, the number of pilgrims rapidly grew. The concept of visiting sacred sites or places of particular importance was by no means a new one: Pilgrimage to the Temple in Jerusalem three times a year was one of the most important commandments of Judaism until the destruction of the Temple, and similar injunctions also existed in the local pagan religions. When this custom developed among the Christians, the pilgrimage sites included places associated with earlier traditions of sanctity. The Church of the Holy Sepulcher was regarded as the "New Jerusalem" and took the place of the destroyed Temple. Other major sites where events connected with the Jewish people's past had taken place, such as Mount Sinai, became important places on the pilgrimage map as well. Even pagan sites associated with healing became part of the traditions of miracle-working in Christianity. For example, at the Bethesda Pool, where according to the Gospels, Jesus healed the paralyzed man, a temple of Asclepius, the god of medicine, was unearthed.

The motivation for pilgrimage was not mere curiosity or interest, but rather, the pilgrims' desire to see, touch, and breathe the air of the holy places and thereby fully experience their faith. Standing at these commemorative sites, they could identify with the figures they venerated and imagine that they themselves had participated in the fateful events of the past; when they touched the stones, they felt that they imbibed something of their sanctity, the property of holiness being transmittable by physical touch. It was in this spirit that the ceremonial rites were established: the prayers, the processions, the presentation of holy relics and their adoration, the performance of symbolic acts, and the reading of the relevant scriptural passages.

Our main source of knowledge on pilgrimage, on the routes taken, and on the length of the journeys is the pilgrimage literature that has come down to us. Most of the travelers whose writings have survived were westerners who wrote in Latin. The descriptions of their journeys are not particularly literary, and they vary in type and style: some chiefly record the routes and their distances, while others stress the experience of the visit.

The first piece of writing to include a description of the holy places is that of the Bordeaux pilgrim, who made a pilgrimage in 333 CE. A better-known account, however, is that of Egeria, a nun from western Spain, who visited the Holy Land about fifty years later. Egeria spent several years in the eastern Mediterranean region, about three of these in Jerusalem. Her descriptions, which are addressed to her "sisters in grace" in Europe, are long and detailed, and are chiefly concerned with liturgical practices and ceremonies. The image that emerges from these writings is that of a woman familiar with the Scriptures, extremely devout, full of curiosity, fond of traveling, and undaunted by the difficulties of the journey. Her writings manage to convey the excitement of visiting the holy places and give a sense of what it was like to participate in the liturgical processions. Another important text is that of the Piacenza pilgrim from Italy, erroneously called Antoninus. He visited this country in the second half of the sixth century, and his journey also included Sinai, Egypt, and Mesopotamia. The Piacenza pilgrim provides numerous descriptions of tombs of saints, and he is especially concerned with the miracles associated with the sacred relics at various sites. His account is a fascinating testimony to the pilgrims' patterns of behavior, and to the customs that were already in existence in his time and which subsequently became accepted practice.

The writings of these travelers exhibit a deep familiarity with the Holy Scriptures, and in fact, the pilgrims may have taken copies of the Scriptures along with them on their journeys. The pilgrims probably had no maps, and it may be assumed that they relied upon local guides. However, it seems that such maps did exist, the most outstanding evidence of this being the mosaic map discovered on the floor of a sixth-century church at Madaba in Jordan. This map points out the major sites of the Holy Land and indicates the important events that took place at each one, sometimes also quoting relevant verses from the Bible. The various settlements are generally depicted in a rather stereotyped fashion, but in some cases, the picture is based on reality. In the depiction of Jerusalem, for example, one can identify major buildings in the city.

Pilgrims in front of the Church of the Holy Sepulcher, 19th century

Jerusalem was the main destination of every pilgrimage, even though it was reached via many different routes. Those who came from the north along the coastal route visited Dor, Caesarea, and Jaffa before they went up to Jerusalem via Lydda-Diospolis, the town of St. George, and Emmaus. Many went by sea to Alexandria, and from there traveled to Jerusalem by way of Gaza, Ashkelon, and Beth Guvrin (Eleutheropolis). Another route was from Damascus, via the Jordan Valley and Beth Shean (Scythopolis). Other destinations in the Holy Land were the Galilee and the northern shore of the Sea of Galilee, Sebaste and Mt. Gerizim in Samaria, and – south of Jerusalem – Bethlehem and Mamre; some even traveled as far as the Negev and Sinai. On the way, the pilgrims required accommodations and various services, and this naturally increased the importance of the sites near the main roads. It is likely that the towns of the Negev, with their many churches, developed because of the need to provide services to pilgrims, being important stations on the way to Sinai, and as such they became religious centers in their own right. Pilgrims also visited sites sacred to Christianity in Asia Minor, Syria, and Egypt.

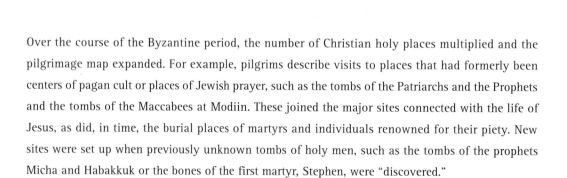

Inscription modeled in plaster, found in a cistern of the Nea Church, the Old City of Jerusalem:
"This work too was donated by our most pious Emperor Flavius Justinian, through the provision and care of Constantine, most saintly priest and abbot, in the 13th year of the indiction."
The construction of the church by Justinian is described in detail by the contemporaneous historian Procopius. The year referred to is apparently 524/5.

Over the course of the Byzantine period, the number of Christian holy places multiplied and the pilgrimage map expanded. For example, pilgrims describe visits to places that had formerly been centers of pagan cult or places of Jewish prayer, such as the tombs of the Patriarchs and the Prophets and the tombs of the Maccabees at Modiin. These joined the major sites connected with the life of Jesus, as did, in time, the burial places of martyrs and individuals renowned for their piety. New sites were set up when previously unknown tombs of holy men, such as the tombs of the prophets Micha and Habakkuk or the bones of the first martyr, Stephen, were "discovered."

An important role was played by the sacred relics preserved in the churches, which became drawing points for pilgrims and around which liturgical ceremonies developed. The relics were objects connected with events that had occurred at the sites, bones of saints who were buried there, or pieces of clothing or objects of religious significance that had been brought from other places. During the Byzantine period, the practice of transferring relics from one place to another developed, sometimes even in the face of the explicit objection of the community whose relics were being removed. "Secondary" relics were created by bringing pieces of important objects from one church to another, such as bits of the True Cross, stones from Golgotha, or even hair from a saint's head.

Archaeological excavations have provided evidence of pilgrimage sites not mentioned in pilgrimage literature. For example, a large church discovered at Dor contained evidence of a cult of saints, and a church unearthed at Rehovot-in-the-Negev had a crypt with a place for a reliquary. The fact that there are stairs leading down to the crypt on both its sides indicates that organized ceremonies were held at the site.

As mentioned above, the climax of every pilgrimage was the visit to Jerusalem, with its many churches and commemorative buildings. Apparently, there was no fixed or obligatory route for visiting the city's numerous sites; sometimes, the order was simply determined by the way the traveler entered the city. We have a relatively large amount of information about the sacred buildings in Jerusalem, not only from pilgrimage literature but also from ecclesiastical writings. It seems that the ceremonies held at major churches drew many participants, attesting to a large number of pilgrims and clergymen. Many of the pilgrims were people of means and high social standing, and quite a number of them remained in the country and became monks. When they died, they left their assets to the Church, or ordered that a new church or monastery be founded with the funds. Ordinary pilgrims also donated generous sums to the sacred edifices, which thus accumulated great wealth.

The fascinating nature of Christian pilgrimage to the Holy Land is also attested by the small objects produced especially for pilgrims. These objects – the material expression of the spiritual and ritual experience of pilgrimage – represented the blessing (*eulogia* in Greek) that the site or the sacred relic bestowed upon the pilgrim, which he or she could take away with him. Such objects were generally small flasks containing oil from the lamps that burnt in the churches or at the sacred tombs, or oil that had come into contact with the relics at the holy places. Tokens made from earth from the holy places served as a means of protection for travelers on their way home and were used as remedies for ills and misfortunes of all kinds. These objects bore scenes from the life of Jesus and depictions of the miracles he performed, which increased their efficacy.

When one goes westward out of the city one passes through David's Gate, which
is on a gentle slope of Mount Zion. Then, as one keeps Mount Zion on
the left, there is a stone bridge supported by arches which runs due south
through the valley.

Adomnan, on the holy places

The Entry to Jerusalem

To accommodate the many pilgrims that arrived in Jerusalem, lodgings and other facilities, such as bathhouses, shops for the sale of souvenirs and amulets, and so forth, were essential. Excavations near Jerusalem's gates, along the main routes that led to the city, have revealed various buildings, which undoubtedly served such purposes.

Jerusalem has always been most easily accessed from the north, where the approach is relatively level. Over the past century, excavations of this route, which leads to the Damascus Gate, have uncovered the remains of numerous buildings, among them monasteries and hospices for pilgrims. Of particular importance was the monastery of St. Stephen, the first martyr, whose bones were discovered by chance and brought for burial at the site where he was stoned to death (Acts 7:58–59). Near the site is an additional monastery established by Armenians, as the inscriptions found in its vicinity suggest.

Pilgrims traveling by way of the coastal road in the west, and those who arrived from the south, from the area of Bethlehem and Hebron, entered Jerusalem at the Jaffa Gate. There, two of Jerusalem's most important aqueducts were located. Excavations have also revealed in this area a large bathhouse, as well as the remains of various workshops. Along the road leading up to the gate, a row of shops was discovered. It is likely that the plaza in front of the gate was filled with street vendors and that lively commerce was conducted at the site. Literary sources indicate that monks serving at the Church of the Holy Sepulcher lived in this part of the city.

Reconstruction of the vicinity of the Jaffa Gate, Jerusalem, in the Byzantine period. Within the city, the Church of the Holy Sepulcher, the Nea Church, and the Zion Church are visible.

Opposite: Detail of the reconstruction

Not far from the city gates, cemeteries were situated. Near the Jaffa Gate, a particularly large burial cave was found. Before it stood a chapel decorated with wall paintings and mosaics. In this cave, victims of the massacre that took place during the time of the Persian invasion of 614 were probably buried.

"For the redemption and salvation of those, God knows their names." Greek inscription on the mosaic floor of the burial chapel excavated in Mamilla, west of the Jaffa Gate, Jerusalem. This formula was customary on anonymous tombs of the Byzantine period and was used to reconstruct the missing parts of the inscription.

"I, Ewestat the priest, laid this mosaic. (You), who enter this house, remember me and my brother Luke to Christ." Armenian mosaic inscription from the monastery north of the Damascus Gate, Jerusalem.

Mosaic floor of the 6th-century Armenian burial chapel near the
Damascus Gate, Jerusalem

Following pages: Reconstruction of
the vicinity of the Damascus Gate,
Jerusalem, in the Byzantine period

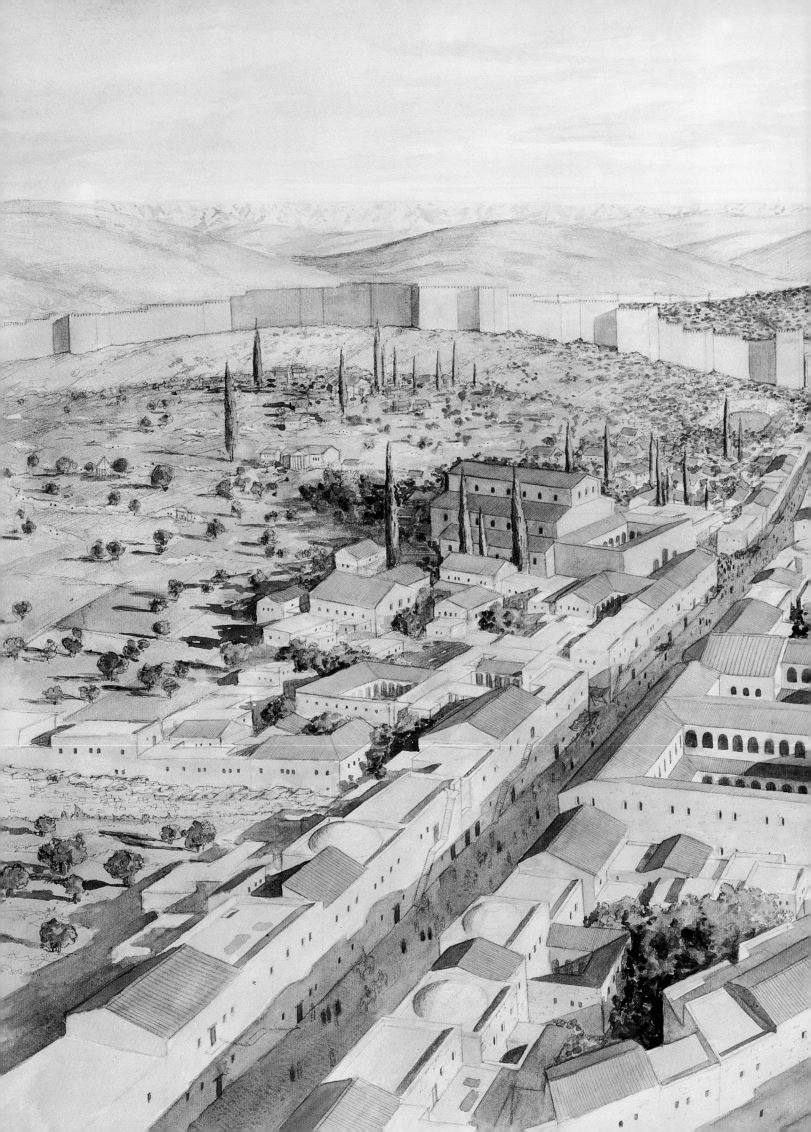

Oil of the Tree of Life from the Holy Places
Inscription on a lead ampulla

Eulogia Vessels

One of the aims of the pilgrims when they visited the holy places was to take something of the blessing – *eulogia* in Greek – inherent in the site back home with them, to serve as a means of protection or cure. These "blessings" often consisted of oil from the lamps that burned at the holy places, water from the Jordan River, or earth from a place associated with a saint. To transport these substances, a variety of containers were designed, among them flat, two-handled flasks known as *eulogia* flasks or ampullae (sing. ampulla), which were made of pottery, metal, or glass.

A remarkable group of ampullae made of an alloy of lead and zinc was preserved among the treasures of a church at Monza, Italy and in the monastery of the adjacent town of Bobbio. Based on the inscriptions and scenes from the life of Jesus depicted on them, it is assumed that these flasks came from the Church of the Holy Sepulcher in Jerusalem and date from the sixth to seventh century. The Langobard queen Theodolinda (died 625), whose capital was at Monza, apparently donated the flasks to the city's monastery. The simpler pottery ampullae served the same purpose as the more elaborate ones, but the sites with which they were associated cannot always be ascertained.

Among the ampullae that can be ascribed to specific sites, those of St. Menas, whose pilgrimage center was in Abu Mina, west of Alexandria, are particularly prominent. Many such flasks have been found in Israel. It is possible that they were brought into the country by pilgrims who traveled by sea to Alexandria and continued over land to the holy places, stopping at the monastery of St. Menas on the way. Other ampullae unearthed in Israel come from Asia Minor – apparently from the church of John the Apostle at Ephesus – or from Qal'at Sem'an in northern Syria, which was a large pilgrimage center of St. Symeon Stylites, who lived on top of a column.

The Piacenza pilgrim describes the process by which the holiness from the True Cross in the Church of the Holy Sepulcher was imparted to flasks of oil: "They offer oil to be blessed in little flasks. When the mouth of one of the little flasks touches the Wood of the Cross, the oil instantly bubbles over, and unless it is closed very quickly it all spills out."

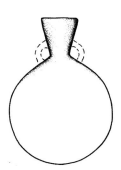

Opposite:
Metal ampullae of the Monza type.
Above left: The Crucifixion, with only Jesus' head visible above the cross, flanked by the two robbers who were crucified with him. Inscription: "Oil of the Tree of Life from the holy places to Christ."
Above right: The Women beside the Empty Tomb. To the right, an angel. Inscription: "The Lord has risen."
Below left: The Nativity, showing the infant Jesus in a cradle. Above, a star, and flanking him, an ox and an ass. To the right, Mary, and to the left, Joseph. Inscription: "Emanuel, God is with us."
Below right: The Baptism, portraying Jesus in the water, with John the Baptist to the right, and an angel to the left. Inscription: "Blessing (*eulogia*) of the Lord from the holy places."

Left: Pottery ampulla of St. Symeon Stylites, from Caesarea.
Right: Pottery ampulla from Asia Minor, found in excavations outside the Jaffa Gate, Jerusalem.

Pottery ampullae from the Holy Land. The decoration consists mainly of lines and dots.

St. Menas ampullae. Menas is depicted in an attitude of prayer (as an orant), with his arms outspread. Flanking him are two recumbent camels.

Glass vessels decorated with the image of a saint on a column (Stylites)

Above and opposite: Glass vessels bearing faces or in the shape of human heads, possibly *eulogia* vessels

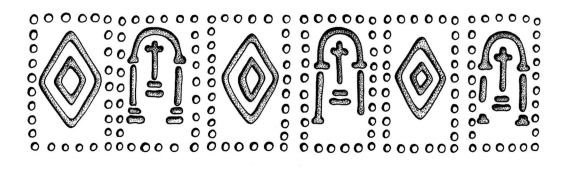

Glass jar decorated with crosses. The jar belongs to a group of hexagonal and octagonal glass vessels bearing religious symbols (both Jewish and Christian), which were used for taking water and oil from the holy places. They were apparently produced in Jerusalem in the late 6th – early 7th century. The motifs on this jar are represented upside-down.

Pottery *eulogia* juglets
found in Jerusalem

Miniature lead vessels,
possibly *eulogia* vessels

Oil Juglets and Lamps

The small jugs with a single handle and a spout were presumably used to fill lamps with oil. Their decorations are practically identical to those on the *eulogia* flasks, indicating that they were produced in the same workshops. Like the flasks, the juglets were made in molds, and most are decorated with human faces in high relief. On some of them, the face takes up the entire surface of the vessel, while on others, it is smaller. The similarity between the juglets and the flasks may indicate that the vessels played a role in a special ceremony in which oil from the lamps that burned at the holy places was transferred to individual *eulogia* flasks. If this theory is correct, it is possible that the faces appearing on such vessels were believed to represent individuals associated with the sites from which the oil was taken.

Some of the simple pottery oil lamps bear Christian symbols together with human faces and images that cannot be identified, though it may be assumed that these images were meaningful to the people who used the lamps. The figure of an orant – a person praying with uplifted arms – which appears on some of the lamps could have represented anyone and does not necessarily refer to a specific person.

Opposite:
Group of pottery juglets used for pouring oil

Oil lamps bearing faces or human figures: the handle of the one to the right is cross-shaped and surmounted by a head (perhaps representing the Crucifixion); the bottom lamp is decorated with two heads, two figures in an attitude of prayer, and crosses; the lamps above and to the left are identical, only differing in the decoration of the handles.

Eulogia Tokens

The most common pilgrimage objects of the Byzantine period are the *eulogia* tokens, which bear a variety of scenes. The tokens are lumps of earth or clay taken from the holy places, which were stamped with scenes related to the events that occurred at the sites, or to the saints that lived there. They were not souvenirs in the modern sense of the word, but rather a means of transporting a blessing from the holy place, for use as remedy against all sorts of calamities– from illness to storms at sea.

Apart from simply holding the tokens, it was also common to scrape their edges (the tokens were fired at low temperatures and thus crumbled easily) and, for example, scatter the resulting dust over the endangered area or mix it with some sort of liquid, to be ingested as medicine. The protective qualities of the tokens lay not only in the material from which they were made, but also in the scenes they bore. Many scenes are clearly attributable to specific holy places. The Adoration of the Magi, for example, can be attributed to Bethlehem; the Baptism – to the Church of John the Baptist in Samaria; the Two Marys beside the Empty Tomb – to the Church of the Holy Sepulcher. In certain cases, it is not possible to attribute the tokens to a specific holy place; nevertheless, the scenes they bear indicate that they had remedial or protective value.

One type of token bears an image that is difficult to interpret, surrounded by the Greek inscription "Solomon." King Solomon was believed to be capable of fighting all sorts of demons and spirits, and according to tradition, he kept, beneath his signet ring, a special root known for its wondrous qualities. It has recently been proposed that the strange image depicted on the token represents this root, which some scholars have identified as the mandrake root, and that such tokens were made from earth from Solomon's Tomb, which in Byzantine times was believed to be south of Bethlehem.

Opposite:
Glass bowl with 80 tokens bearing a variety of scenes. The origin of the bowl and its contents is not known, but is attributed to Syria. Owing to the great diversity of the scenes, it is unlikely that all the tokens were produced in a single place. This may have been the collection of a peddler or pilgrim, which was assembled over the course of his travels.

"Solomon" token

Syrian tokens, one bearing the image of St. Symeon Stylites and the other a depiction of the Entry into Jerusalem, along with the Greek inscription: "St. Sergius." The center of St. Sergius was in northern Syria.

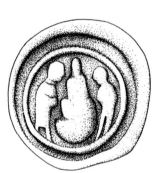

Various tokens from Beth Shean and Samaria. Above left: The Apparition of Jesus on the road to Emmaus. Above right: The Adoration of the Magi. Below left: The Ascension. Below right: The Baptism.

List of Objects in the Catalogue

This list includes details of all the objects illustrated in the catalogue, given in the following order: name; provenance (the precise provenance is not always known, though most of the items were discovered in Israel or its environs); date ("Byzantine period" refers to the 4th–7th century); dimensions (one dimension only, to provide an indication of size; measurements are in centimeters: H = height, D = diameter, L = length); ownership of the object and its number in the collection.

Many of the objects are published here for the first time. Those that have already appeared in publications are accompanied by bibliographic references. Where possible, the first publication of the object is noted, as well as a later publication containing a more detailed bibliography. The list is arranged by pages; the objects on each page are referred to in the following order: above from left to right, and below from left to right.

The Historical Jesus

(p. 18)
Ossuary of "Jesus / Jesus (Yeshua) son of Joseph"
Jerusalem, 1st century CE
Stone, L 58
Israel Antiquities Authority, S.767
Rahmani 1994, no. 9

Ossuary of "Judas son of Jesus (Yeshua)"
East Talpiyyot, Jerusalem, 1st century CE
Stone, L 54
Israel Antiquities Authority, 80-501
Rahmani 1994, no. 702

(p. 19)
"Martha," Hebrew inscription on an ossuary
Givat Hamivtar, Jerusalem, 1st century CE
Stone, L of inscription 13.5
Israel Antiquities Authority, 68-681
Rahmani 1994, no. 220

"Mary," Hebrew inscription on an ossuary
East Talpiyyot, Jerusalem, 1st century CE
Stone, L of inscription 12
Israel Antiquities Authority, 80-505
Rahmani 1994, no. 706

"Matthew," Hebrew inscription on an ossuary
Talbiyeh, Jerusalem, 1st century CE
Stone, L of inscription 18
Israel Antiquities Authority, 36.1869
Rahmani 1994, no. 72

"Judas," Greek inscription on an ossuary
Mount of Olives, Jerusalem, 1st century CE
Stone, L of inscription 16.5
Israel Antiquities Authority, S. 2581
Rahmani 1994, no. 32

"Jesus son of Alot," Greek inscription on an ossuary
Mount of Olives, Jerusalem, 1st century CE
Stone, L of inscription 35
Israel Antiquities Authority, 46.174
Rahmani 1994, no. 114

(p. 20)

Large jar (a)
Ophel excavations, Jerusalem,
1st century CE
Stone, H 82
Israel Antiquities Authority, I.2222

Large jar (b)
Western Wall excavations, Jerusalem,
1st century CE
Stone, H 76
Israel Antiquities Authority, 99-3982
Magen 1994, 251

Large jar (c)
Western Wall excavations, Jerusalem,
1st century CE
Stone, H 75
Israel Antiquities Authority, 99-4050

Large jar (d)
Mount Zion, Jerusalem, 1st century CE
Stone, H 67
Israel Antiquities Authority, 92-844

Large jar (e)
Jewish Quarter, Jerusalem, 1st century CE
Stone, H 63
Israel Antiquities Authority, 91-461

Large jar (f)
Hagay Street, Jerusalem, 1st century CE
Stone, H 55
Israel Antiquities Authority, 31.175
Hamilton 1931, 108

(p. 21)
Thanksgiving Scroll
Qumran, 1st century BCE –
1st century CE
Parchment, L 75
The Israel Museum, Jerusalem, Shrine of the Book, 95.57.24A
Licht 1956

(p. 22)
Fragment of a parapet from the Temple enclosure
Hebrew inscription: "To the place of trumpeting ..."
Western Wall excavations, Jerusalem, 1st century CE
Stone, L 86
Israel Antiquities Authority, 78-1439
Inscriptions Reveal 1973, no. 168

(p. 23)
Fragmentary Greek inscription forbidding entry to the Temple
Near the Lions' Gate, Jerusalem,
1st century CE
Stone, H 49
Israel Antiquities Authority, 36.989
Inscriptions Reveal 1973, no. 169

Ossuary of "Joseph son of Caiaphas"
North Talpiyyot, Jerusalem, 1st century CE
Stone, L 74
Israel Antiquities Authority, 91-468
Greenhut 1992, 65–68; Reich 1992

(p. 24)
Latin dedicatory inscription of
Pontius Pilate
Roman theater at Caesarea, 26–36 CE
Stone, H 80
Israel Antiquities Authority, 61-521
Inscriptions Reveal 1973, no. 216

(p. 25)
Ankle bone with a nail
Givat Hamivtar, Jerusalem, 1st century CE
Bone, wood, and iron, L of nail 12
Israel Antiquities Authority, 95-2067/5
Haas 1970; Zias and Sekeles 1985

Ossuary of "Yehohanan son of Hagkol"
Givat Hamivtar, Jerusalem, 1st century CE
Stone, L 57
Israel Antiquities Authority, 68-679
Tzaferis 1970, 35–36; Yadin 1973

I
The Spread of Christianity
in the Holy Land

(p. 33)
Ostracon inscribed with the
Christian creed
Provenance unknown
Pottery, H 16
The Israel Museum, Jerusalem,
Hertz Collection, 69.74.312
Ullmann 1996, 194, figs. 3–4

(p. 34)
Ornamented cross (crux gemmata)
Caesarea, 6th–7th century
Painting on dry plaster (secco),
H of cross 76
Israel Antiquities Authority, 2000-804
Patrich 1996, 170–71, figs. 23–24

(p. 40)
Column with a niche for a sacred relic
Church at Dor, Byzantine period
Marble, H of pillar 192, H of inscription 25
Israel Antiquities Authority, 52-1153
Leibovitch 1953

(p. 42)
Chancel screen with a depiction of the
cross on Golgotha
Church at Horvat Bata, Carmiel,
6th century
Limestone, H 99
Israel Antiquities Authority, 92-267/8

(p. 43)
Handle with an impression of the
ornamented cross (crux gemmata)
on Golgotha
Provenance unknown, Byzantine period
Pottery, H 9
Israel Antiquities Authority, 42.413

(p. 44)
Ring with a scene of the Two Women
beside the Empty Tomb
Provenance unknown, 6th–7th century
Bronze, D 2.3
Royal Ontario Museum, Toronto,
986.181.26
Maguire et al. 1989, no. 89

Silver bracelet with Christian motifs
(see description of p. 162)

Censer with scenes from the life of Jesus
Provenance unknown, 6th–7th century
Bronze, H 10.5
University of Toronto, Malcove
Collection, M 82.410
Campbell 1985, no. 118

II
The Architecture and Liturgy
of the Early Church

(p. 48)
Dedicatory plaque with a cross, two birds,
and a Greek inscription:
"For the salvation of Zechariah and his
son Stephen"
Provenance unknown, Byzantine period
Marble, L 62
Collection of the Wolff Family, Jerusalem

(p. 54)
Altar (see description of pp. 56–57, c)

(p. 55)
Ambo (pulpit; see description of
pp. 56–57, q)

Ambo (pulpit)
Church of St. Theodore, Khirbet Beit Sila,
6th century
Bituminous stone, H of panels 77
Staff Archaeological Officer in the Civil
Administration of Judea and Samaria,
K28908-28909, K29518, K30188, K30189
Batz, forthcoming

(pp. 56–57)
Reconstruction of a church bema
(presbytery)

Cross (a)
Western Wall excavations, Jerusalem,
Byzantine period
Bronze, H 63
Israel Antiquities Authority, 99-3893
Mazar 1998, 19 (Hebrew)

Mosaic floor (b)
Apse of the church at Castra,
Carmel coast, 5th century
Stone, D 450
Israel Antiquities Authority, 95-1677,
96-1807
Yeivin and Finkielsztejn 1999, 24*, fig. 44

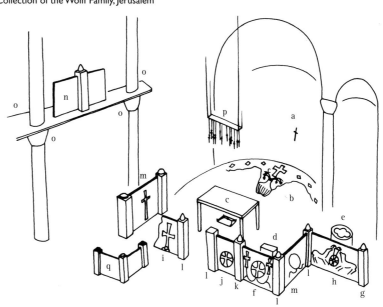

Altar (c)
Church of the monastery at Khirbet
ed-Deir, Judean Desert
Marble, H 111
Staff Archaeological Officer in the Civil
Administration of Judea and Samaria,
K29519
Habas 1999, 119–23

Lectern (d)
Church at Horvat Hesheq, Western
Galilee, 6th century
Stone, L 60
Israel Antiquities Authority 99-3469
Aviam 1990, 359, fig. 10

Baptismal font (e)
Central church at Lower Herodium,
6th century
Stone, D 100
Staff Archaeological Officer in the Civil
Administration of Judea and Samaria,
K030582
Netzer et al. 1993, 229

Chancel screen with a cross-flower inside
a wreath in relief (f)
Massuot Yizhaq, Northern Negev,
Byzantine period
Marble, H 92
Israel Antiquities Authority, 53-4
Treasures 1986, no. 132

Chancel-screen post (g)
Massuot Yizhaq, Northern Negev,
Byzantine period
Marble, H 118
Israel Antiquities Authority, 63-845

Chancel screen with a cross-amphora
flanked by deer in relief (h)
Hebron hill region, Byzantine period
Stone, H 107
Staff Archaeological Officer in the Civil
Administration of Judea and Samaria,
T15587

Chancel screen with a cross on Golgotha
in relief (i)
Church at Horvat Bata, Carmiel,
Byzantine period
Stone, H 100
Israel Antiquities Authority, 98-2676

Chancel screen with a cross in relief (j)
Church at Horvat Bata, Carmiel,
Byzantine period
Stone, H 100
Israel Antiquities Authority, 81-506

Chancel-screen post (k)
Church at Horvat Bata, Carmiel,
Byzantine period
Stone, H 125
Israel Antiquities Authority, 98-2681

Chancel-screen posts (l)
Beersheba, Byzantine period
Marble, H 100–120
Israel Antiquities Authority, 99-114,
99-117, 99-118, 99-2395

Chancel screens with crosses and wreaths
in relief and chancel-screen posts (m)
Martyr's Church at Tel Iztabba, northern
Beth Shean, Byzantine period
Marble, H 90–97
Israel Antiquities Authority, 99-4486-9
Mazor and Bar-Natan 1996, fig. 37

Two slabs and a post, carved and
painted red (n)
Gallery balustrade of the church at
Horvat Hesheq, Western Galilee,
6th century
Stone, H of panel 78
Israel Antiquities Authority, 99-3465-7
Aviam 1990, 360–64, figs. 16–18

Column bases and capitals with crosses
inside wreaths (o)
Ashdod-Yam, Byzantine period
H of the capitals 43, H of the bases
14–17
Israel Antiquities Authority, 99-2395-6,
99-4399, 99-4400

Crosses and Christograms on chains (p)
Churches in the Western Galilee (Evron,
Nahariyya, Shavei Ziyyon, and Khirbet
el-Waziya), 5th–6th century
Bronze
Israel Antiquities Authority 51-251, 51-
956-958, 57-795, 63-2715, 74-2049-55, 97-
4185, 74-2065-66, 97-4574
Prausnitz 1967, pl. 18 b,c; Dauphin and
Edelstein 1984, figs. 26–28, pls. 50, 59–60;
Aviam 1995, 53 (Hebrew)

Ambo (q)
Martyr's Church at Tel Iztabba, northern
Beth Shean, 6th century
Marble, H of slabs 88
Israel Antiquities Authority, 99-4482-4485
Bar-Natan and Mazor 1992, fig. 70

(p. 59)
Two carved and painted slabs and a post
from a gallery balustrade (see description
of pp. 56–57, n)

(p. 61)
Baptismal font (see description of
pp. 56–57, e)

(p. 62)
Capital with crosses
Ashdod-Yam, Byzantine period
Stone, H 25
Israel Antiquities Authority, 99-130

Capital with crosses surmounting
amphorae
Church near Mazzuva, Western Galilee,
Byzantine period
Stone, H 48
Israel Antiquities Authority, 99-4379

(p. 65)
Capital with crosses inside aediculae
Provenance unknown, Byzantine period
Stone, H 52
Studium Biblicum Franciscanum Museum,
Jerusalem

(p. 68)
Chancel screen with vine scrolls, grape
clusters, and birds in relief
Northern church at Nizzana,
5th–6th century
Stone, H 73
Israel Antiquities Authority, 40.284
Colt 1962, 49–50, pl. XIX:1

(p. 69)
Chancel screen with a bird in relief,
fragment
Church at Shavei Ziyyon, 5th–6th century
Marble, H 30
Israel Antiquities Authority, 99-4374
Prausnitz 1967, pl. XVII:a

(p. 70)
Chancel screen with a cross-amphora
flanked by deer in relief
(see description of pp. 56–57, h)

(p. 71)
Chancel screen with a deer beside a
cross in relief, fragment
Provenance unknown, 6th century
Marble, H 57
Israel Antiquities Authority, 445176-9

(p. 72)
Chancel screen with the portrait of a
saint, fragment
Church at Nahariyya, 6th century
Marble, H 26
Israel Antiquities Authority, 9-4371
Dauphin and Edelstein 1984, 31, pl. 10:b

Chancel screen with a cross-flower
inside a wreath in relief (see description
of pp. 56–57, f)

(p. 73)
Chancel screen with a ram and the cross
on the hillock of Golgotha in relief,
fragment
Horvat Karkara, Western Galilee,
5th–6th century
Marble, H 28
Israel Antiquities Authority, 99-3468
Aviam 1994, 70, fig. 130 (Hebrew)

Chancel screen with a relief of a lamp or
a censer suspended in an *aedicula*
Susita, 6th century
Marble, H 87
Israel Antiquities Authority, 52-710
Anati 1957, 32, pl. IV:2 (Hebrew)

(p. 74)
Sigma-shaped, multi-lobed table
Central church(?) at Lower Herodium,
6th century
Bituminous stone, L 102
Staff Archaeological Officer in the Civil
Administration of Judea and Samaria,
K31271

Sigma-shaped table with a cross
Tel Masos, Eastern Negev, Byzantine
period
Stone, L 84
Israel Antiquities Authority, 99-115
Aharoni et al. 1975, pl. 9:b

(p. 75)
Lectern (see description of pp. 56–57, d)

(p. 76)
Reliquary with a spout
Horvat Hesheq, Western Galilee,
Byzantine period
Stone and copper, L 27
Israel Antiquities Authority, 99-3470
Aviam 1990, 360–61, figs. 12–13

Reliquary in the shape of a miniature
sarcophagus
Church of St. Theodore at Khirbet
Beit Sila, 6th century
Marble, L 16.5
Staff Archaeological Officer in the Civil
Administration of Judea and Samaria,
K030581
Batz, forthcoming

Reliquary divided into two
compartments, with a perforated lid
Kfar Rami, Upper Galilee, Byzantine period
Stone, L 25
Israel Antiquities Authority, 69-5339

(p. 77)
Reliquary decorated with crosses, with a
sliding lid
Eastern Mediterranean, 5th–7th century
Marble, L 21
Collection of Christian Schmidt,
Munich, 172
Wamser and Zahlhaas 1998, 24–25, no. 11

(p. 78)
Mosaic floor with depictions of hunting
scenes and animals and an inscription in
Greek
Church at Kissufim, Negev, 576–578(?)
Stone and glass, L 800
Israel Antiquities Authority, 77-416
Cohen 1993

(p. 80)
Relief of a figure (Jesus?) blessing
Hanita, Western Galilee, 6th century
Marble, L 55
Israel Antiquities Authority, 93-1518
Barash 1986 (Hebrew)

Part of a mosaic floor depicting vegetal
scrolls and animals
Church at Khirbet el-Waziya,
Western Galilee
Stone, L 480
Israel Antiquities Authority, 91-435/2
Aviam 1995, 52–55 (Hebrew)

(p. 81)
Square tile with an elaborate cross design
Provenance unknown, 6th–7th century
Gold-glass, L 9
The Israel Museum, Jerusalem, 77.12.321
Spaer, forthcoming, no. 615

(p. 82)
Plaques with portraits of saints
Rehovot-in-the-Negev, 5th–6th century
Painted glass, D 6.5
Israel Antiquities Authority, 77-91, 77-92
Tsafrir et al. 1988, 142–49

Wall painting depicting three saints
as orants
Vaulted storeroom, Caesarea,
late 6th – early 7th century
Paint on dry plaster (secco), L 330
Israel Antiquities Authority, 2000-803
Avner 1999

(p. 84)
Chalice
Beth Shean, Byzantine period
Pottery, H 6
Israel Antiquities Authority, 52-131

Chalice
Church at Beth Yerah, 5th–7th century
Glass, H 10
Israel Antiquities Authority, 53-189

Jug
Helez, Northern Negev, 4th–5th century
Glass, H 32
Israel Antiquities Authority, 59-20

(p. 85)
Flat spoon with crosses and a Greek
inscription: "Petrus"
Eastern Mediterranean, 6th century
Silver and niello, L 18
Royal Ontario Museum, Toronto,
986.181.94
Maguire et al. 1989, no. 63

(pp. 86–87)
Part of a mosaic floor with a depiction of
two women
Church at Kissufim, Negev, 6th century
Stone, H 104
Israel Antiquities Authority, 77-416/13-14
Cohen 1993; Di Segni 1997, no. 231

(p. 88)
Chalice with a Greek dedicatory inscription
Hama, Syria, 6th century
Silver, H 19
Musée Sainte-Anne, Pérès Blancs,
Jerusalem, PB3715
Mango 1986, no. 27

Strainer with a Greek inscription:
"Of St. Sergius"
Hama, Syria, 6th century
Silver, L 14.5
Musée Sainte-Anne, Pérès Blancs,
Jerusalem, PB3716
Mango 1986, no. 26

(p. 89)
Ladle-strainer with a cross
Provenance unknown, 5th–6th century
Silver and enamel, H 15
University of Toronto, Malcove
Collection, M82.428
Campbell 1985, no. 84

Spoons with crosses on the handle ends
Provenance unknown, Byzantine period
Silver, L 23, 16.5
Collection of Shlomo Moussaieff, Herzliya
and London

Spoon with an engraved decoration
Caesarea, 5th–6th century
Silver, L 15
Israel Antiquities Authority, 95-1635
Patrich, forthcoming

(p. 90)
Processional cross with a depiction of
Jesus and saints
Greek dedicatory inscription: "For the
forgiveness of the sins of Leontia"
Syria-Palestine, 6th–7th century
Bronze, H 18
Dumbarton Oaks, Washington, D.C., 69.75
Cotsonis 1994, no. 9

Processional cross with a depiction of
Jesus, Mary, and angels
Greek dedicatory inscription: "In
fulfillment of the vow of Leontius"
Syria-Palestine, 6th–7th century
Bronze, H 16
Royal Ontario Museum, Toronto,
994.220.11
Cotsonis 1994, no. 8

(p. 91)
Chalice engraved with a depiction of the
adoration of the cross
Syria-Palestine, 6th century
Glass, D 15
Dumbarton Oaks, Washington, D.C., 37.21
Ross 1962, no. 96; Weitzman 1979, no. 545

(p. 92)
Carved plaque with a depiction of angels
carrying a wreath with a cross in the center
Syria, 6th–8th century
Ivory, L 30
Staatliche Museen zu Berlin,
Skulpturensammlung und Museum für
Byzantinische Kunst, 2978
Weitzman 1979, no. 458

Pyxis with depictions of the Annunciation,
the Nativity, and the Journey to
Bethlehem
Syria-Palestine, 6th century
Ivory, H 8
Staatliche Museen zu Berlin,
Skulpturensammlung und Museum für
Byzantinische Kunst, 585
Weitzman 1979, no. 447

Top of a scepter(?) in the shape of a hand
Church at Dor, 6th century
Ivory, H 10
Israel Antiquities Authority, 52-600
Leibovitch 1957 (Hebrew)

(p. 93)
Carved plaque depicting the Nativity and
the Adoration of the Magi
Eastern Mediterranean, first half of the
6th century
Ivory, H 21.5
Trustees of the British Museum, London,
1904, 7-2, 1
Weitzman 1979, no. 476

(p. 94)
Necklace
Monastery of Lady Mary, Beth Shean,
6th–7th century
Gold, L ca. 75
University of Pennsylvania Museum of
Archaeology and Anthropology,
Philadelphia, 31-50-212
Fitzgerald 1939, 10, pl. 3, fig. 1

(p. 95)
Ten coins
Monastery of Lady Mary, Beth Shean,
6th–7th century
Gold, D 2
University of Pennsylvania Museum of
Archaeology and Anthropology,
Philadelphia, 31-50-391–400
Fitzgerald 1939, 11–13, pl. 4, figs. 1–2

Bracelet
Monastery of Lady Mary, Beth Shean,
6th–7th century
Gold, D 6
University of Pennsylvania Museum of
Archaeology and Anthropology,
Philadelphia, 31-50-213
Fitzgerald 1939, 10

(p. 96)

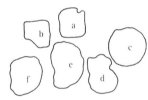

Bread stamp with a Christogram and the
letters *alpha* and *omega* (a)
Provenance unknown, Byzantine period(?)
Stone, L 5.5
Collection of the Wolff Family, Jerusalem

Bread stamp with letters and an
abbreviation of the name Jesus Christ (b)
Provenance unknown, Byzantine period(?)
Stone, L 5
Musée Sainte-Anne, Pérès Blancs,
Jerusalem, PB3668

Bread stamp with the name "Silvanus" in
Greek (c)
Yizream, Northern Negev
Pottery, D 7
Israel Antiquities Authority, 93-1719/1

Bread stamp with an indistinct inscription
and a palm branch
Horvat Gerarit, Negev, Byzantine period
Pottery, D 5
Israel Antiquities Authority, 95-7720

Bread stamp with the letters *alpha* and
omega, and an abbreviation of the name
Jesus Christ (e)
Beth Shean, Byzantine period
Stone, D 7.5
Israel Antiquities Authority, 99-3877

Bread stamp with a cross and four dots (f)
Tel Yenoam, Yavneel Valley, Byzantine
period
Pottery, D 6.6
Israel Antiquities Authority, 83-434

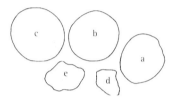

Bread stamp (a)
Tiberias, Early Muslim period(?)
Pottery, D 17
Israel Antiquities Authority, 99-3955
Feig 1994, 591–94, fig. 1

Bread stamp (b)
Tabha, northern Sea of Galilee,
Early Muslim period(?)
Pottery, D 18
Israel Antiquities Authority, 35.3082

Bread stamp (c)
Beth Shean region, Early Muslim period(?)
Pottery, D 18
Israel Antiquities Authority, 97-8538

Bread stamp, fragment (d)
Church at Sebaste, Byzantine period
Stone, L 10
Israel Antiquities Authority, 32.2345
Crowfoot et al. 1957, 466–67, fig. 18:1

Fragment of a bread stamp (e)
Migdal Haemek, Byzantine period
Limestone, D 12.5
Israel Antiquities Authority, 95-3175

(p. 97)
Bread stamp with a cross inside an arch
and a blessing in Greek
Caesarea, 6th century
Pottery, D 10
Israel Antiquities Authority, 99-4431
Patrich 1996, 172, fig. 25; Patrich,
forthcoming

Bread stamp with a blessing in Greek and
a cross on the handle
Provenance unknown, Byzantine period
Pottery, D 7
Musée Sainte-Anne, Pérès Blancs,
Jerusalem, PB3666

(p. 98)
Censer-bowl with chains for suspension
decorated with crosses
Jericho, Byzantine period
Bronze, D 7
Studium Biblicum Franciscanum Museum,
Jerusalem
Bagatti 1939, no. 61

(p. 99)
Censer decorated with crosses, with a
hook for suspension
Provenance unknown, 6th–7th century
Pottery, H 18.5
Israel Antiquities Authority, 71-5076

(p. 100)
Censer-bowl decorated with scenes from
the life of Jesus:
The Annunciation, the Nativity, the
Baptism, the Crucifixion, and the Two
Marys beside the Empty Tomb
Syria, Byzantine period
Bronze, D 7.3
Trustees of the British Museum, London,
MLA72
Dalton 1901, no. 540

Censer-bowl decorated with scenes from
the life of Jesus:
The Annunciation; the Visitation, the
Nativity, the Baptism, the Annunciation to
the Shepherds, and the Crucifixion
Syria-Palestine, ca. 600
Bronze, D 11
Staatliche Museen zu Berlin,
Skulpturensammlung und Museum für
Byzantinische Kunst, 15/69
Weitzman 1979, no. 563

(p. 101)
Censer on a high pedestal with a lid
Provenance unknown, 5th–6th century
Bronze, H 25
University of Toronto, Malcove
Collection, M82.407
Campbell 1985, no. 111

(p. 102)

Censer-bowl with a hook and chains for
suspension (a)
Western Wall excavations, Jerusalem,
6th–7th century
Bronze, H 6
Israel Antiquities Authority, 78-1294
Mazar 1998, 17 (Hebrew)

Hexagonal censer decorated with eagle
heads and animal claws (b)
Provenance unknown, Byzantine period
Bronze, D 7.5
Israel Antiquities Authority, 56-2

Censer-bowl (c)
Shoham, 6th century
Bronze, D 9
Israel Antiquities Authority, 97-4048

Cylindrical censer with a hook and chains
for suspension (d)
Monastery of Lady Mary, Beth Shean,
6th century
Bronze, D 9.5
Israel Antiquities Authority, I.9645
Fitzgerald 1939, 11, pl. 3:2

Censer-bowl (e)
Provenance unknown, Byzantine period
Bronze, D 8.5
Israel Antiquities Authority, 40-1235

Censer-bowl (f)
Beth Shean, Byzantine period
Bronze, D 10
Israel Antiquities Authority, 52-111

Censer-bowl with a hook and chains for
suspension (g)
Yatir, Southern Hebron hill region,
Byzantine period
Bronze, D 8.5
Israel Antiquities Authority, I.4446

Hexagonal censer with a decoration of
circles (h)
Beth Shean, 6th century
Bronze, D 10
Israel Antiquities Authority, M.862
Fitzgerald 1931, 6, 42, pl. 38:24

(p. 103)
Head-shaped censer decorated with
a cross
Eastern Mediterranean, 5th–6th century
Bronze, H 15
Royal Ontario Museum, Toronto,
986.181.110
Maguire et al. 1989, no. 138

(p. 104)
Crosses and Christograms on chains
(see description of pp. 56–57, p)

(p. 105)
Bowl with an engraved cross
Tomb at Bezet, Western Galilee,
5th–6th century
Glass, D 14
Israel Antiquities Authority, 32.2864
Iliffe 1933b, 88, fig. 17

(p. 106)
Hanging device for an oil lamp
Evron, Western Galilee, 6th century
Bronze, L 34
Israel Antiquities Authority, 51-959

Cup-shaped oil lamp with three handles
and a wick holder
Church of the Visitation, Ein Kerem,
6th–7th century(?)
Glass, H 12
Israel Antiquities Authority, 38.2120
Bagatti 1948, 77, fig. 34

Hanging device for an oil lamp
Shelomi, Western Galilee, 6th century
Bronze, H 16.5
Israel Antiquities Authority, 78-2560
Dauphin 1993a, 46

Cup-shaped oil lamp, with three handles
and a wick holder
Eastern Mediterranean, 5th century
Glass, H 8
The Israel Museum, Jerusalem, 69.26.332
Israeli 1998, 51

(p. 107)

Oil lamp on a stand (a)
Beth Shean, 5th–6th century
Bronze, H 28
Israel Antiquities Authority, 52-137
Tzori 1970, 68 (Hebrew)

Oil lamp on a stand (b)
Provenance unknown, 5th–6th century
Bronze, H 48
Israel Antiquities Authority, M.962

Oil lamp on a stand, its lid decorated with
a dove (c)
Syria, 6th century
Bronze, H 34
Collection of Shlomo Moussaieff, Herzliya
and London
Ziffer 1998, 110

Lampstand with animal legs (d)
Givat Zeev, Jerusalem, Byzantine period
Bronze, H 26.5
Staff Archaeological Officer in the Civil
Administration of Judea and Samaria,
K29234

Oil lamp with a lid decorated with a bull's
head (e)
Beth Shean, 5th–6th century
Bronze, L 21
Israel Antiquities Authority, 52-134
Tzori 1970, 68 (Hebrew)

(pp. 108–9)
Chandelier for six oil lamps, with a cross
in the center
Provenance unknown, Byzantine period
Bronze, D 25
Collection of the Wolff Family, Jerusalem

Cup-shaped oil lamp with a stem
Church at Dor, 6th century
Glass, D 8.5
Israel Antiquities Authority, 99-4321

Stems of cup-shaped oil lamps
Church at Dor, 6th century
Glass, H ca. 6
Israel Antiquities Authority, 99-4324, 99-
4326, 99-4331, 99-4329, 99-4333, 99-4337

(p. 110)
Tombstone with an engraved cross
on steps
Shivta, 7th century
Marble, H 55
Israel Antiquities Authority, 47.5351
Negev 1981, no. 59; Di Segni 1997,
no. 341

(p. 112)
Ostracon with a Greek inscription
Shivta, 6th century
Pottery, L 7
Israel Antiquities Authority, 43.154
Youtie 1936

Part of a mosaic floor with a dedicatory
inscription in Greek
Church of the Armenian Monastery,
Damascus Gate, Jerusalem, late 6th –
early 7th century
Stone, L 210
Israel Antiquities Authority, 94-1418/1
Amit and Wolff 1994, 295

(p. 113)
Tombstone of Sophia the deaconess
Mount of Olives, Jerusalem, 6th century
Limestone, L 88
Musée Sainte-Anne, Pérès Blancs,
Jerusalem
Cré 1904; Di Segni 1997, no. 217

III
Christian Images and Symbols

(p. 118)
Double-sided pendant (*enkolpion*)
Eastern Mediterranean, 6th–7th century
Gold, D 7.7
Collection of Christian Schmidt,
Munich, 378
Wamser and Zahlhaas 1998, no. 303

(p. 119)
Octagonal wedding ring
Provenance unknown, Byzantine period
Gold, D 2.3
Collection of Shlomo Moussaieff, Herzliya
and London

Octagonal wedding ring
Provenance unknown, Byzantine period
Gold, D 2, D of plaque 1
Trustees of the British Museum, London,
AF.231
Dalton 1901, no. 129; Vikan 1984, 83,
fig. 25

(p. 120)
Coffin fragment with a Christogram
Provenance unknown, 4th century
Lead, L 26
Israel Antiquities Authority, M.1081
Rahmani 1999a, no. 42

(p. 121)
Oil lamp with a Christogram,
"Beit Natif" type
Provenance unknown, 4th century
Pottery, L 11.5
Studium Biblicum Franciscanum Museum,
Jerusalem

(p. 122)
Oil lamp with a Christogram
North Africa, 4th century
Pottery, L 14
Collection of Shlomo Moussaieff, Herzliya
and London

Oil lamp with a Christogram on the
handle
North Africa, 4th century
Pottery, L 13
Collection of Shlomo Moussaieff, Herzliya
and London

Oil lamp with a Christogram
Shipwreck off the coast of Dor,
4th – early 5th century
Pottery, L 11
Israel Antiquities Authority, 97-488
Sibella 1997

Bowl with a stamped fish motif
Provenance unknown, 4th–5th century
Pottery, D 22
The Israel Museum, Jerusalem, 69.12.559

Bowl with a stamped Christogram
Provenance unknown, 4th–5th century
Pottery, D 17.5
Collection of the Wolff Family, Jerusalem

(p. 123)
Fish-shaped mirror-plaque, used to ward
off the Evil Eye
Tomb at Dikhrin, Judean Foothills,
5th century
Pottery, L 16
Israel Antiquities Authority, 62-286
Rahmani 1964, pl. 16:B

Elaborate fish-shaped oil lamp with a
stamped Christogram and a cross
Provenance unknown, 5th century
Pottery, L 20
Studium Biblicum Franciscanum Museum,
Jerusalem

(p. 124)
Capital with fish and a Christogram
Negev, 5th–6th century
Pottery, H 46
Israel Antiquities Authority, 99-2393
Segal 1988, 238

(p. 126)
Slab with a cross and inscription
Nizzana, 6th century
Stone, L 50.5
Israel Antiquities Authority, 47.5002
Colt 1962, 177–78; Di Segni 1997,
no. 318

(p. 127)
Ampulla with a cross and two birds
Eastern Mediterranean(?), 6th–7th century
Pottery, H 11
Collection of Christian Schmidt,
Munich, 547
Wamser and Zahlhaas 1998, no. 104

(p. 128)
Part of a mosaic floor with a cross, birds,
and a Greek dedicatory inscription
Hazor-Ashdod, 512 CE
H 105
Israel Antiquities Authority, 57-1347/2
Ovadiah 1987, 67–69, pl. LXXIX:2

(p. 129)
Chancel screen(?) fragment with a cross
and a bird
Jericho, Byzantine period
Marble, H 24
Israel Antiquities Authority, 47.5390
Bagatti 1979, 82, pl. 25

Oil lamp with a cross and two birds
Provenance unknown, 4th century
Pottery, L 10
Musée Sainte-Anne, Pérès Blancs,
Jerusalem, PB 0819

Oil lamp with a cross and two birds
Beth Shean, 5th century
Pottery, L 10
Israel Antiquities Authority, 32.167

Mosaic panel with a cross flanked by
two lions(?)
Ozem, Southern Coastal Plain, 6th century
L 153
Israel Antiquities Authority, 56-1390/2-3
Ovadiah 1987, 117, pl. CXXXI

(p. 130)
Chancel screen with a cross encircled
by a wreath
Monastery of Lady Mary, Tel Iztabba,
northern Beth Shean, 6th century
Marble, L 125
Israel Antiquities Authority, I.9632
Fitzgerald 1939, 11, pl. 3:5

Lintel with a cross and inscription
Southern church at Shivta, 6th century
Stone, L 125
Israel Antiquities Authority, 42-256
Kirk 1936, no. 1; Di Segni 1997, no. 324

(p. 131)
Slab with numerous crosses
Amra, Negev, Byzantine period
Stone, H 93
Israel Antiquities Authority, 99-1190
Segal 1988, 236

(p. 132)

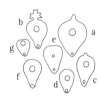

Oil lamp with crosses and the Greek
letters *alpha* and *omega* (a)
Provenance unknown, 7th–8th century
Pottery, L 14
Collection of Shlomo Moussaieff, Herzliya
and London

Oil lamp with a cross (e)
Sebaste, Samaria, Byzantine period
Pottery, L 9.5
Israel Antiquities Authority, I.9880

Oil lamp with a cross and a Greek
inscription: "The light of Christ shines
beautifully for all" (f)
Tomb at Beit Jala, near Bethlehem,
Byzantine period
Pottery, L 10
Israel Antiquities Authority, I.10763

Oil lamps with crosses (b, c, d, g)
Provenance unknown, Byzantine period
Pottery, L 6.5–13
The Israel Museum, Jerusalem, Louis and
Carmen Warschaw Collection, 76.6.1365,
1377, 1403, 1408
Israeli and Avida 1988, nos. 414, 415, 429,
484

(p. 133)
Zoomorphic vessel with a cross
Provenance unknown, 5th–6th century
Pottery, H 15
Collection of Christian Schmidt,
Munich, 59
Wamser and Zahlhaas 1998, no. 168

Oil lamp with a cross
Beth Shean, 4th century
Pottery, L 8
Israel Antiquities Authority, I.9582

Zoomorphic vessel with a cross
Hagosherim, Byzantine period
Pottery, H 15
Israel Antiquities Authority, 66-85

Zoomorphic vessel with an oil lamp
Provenance unknown, Byzantine period
Pottery, H 17
Collection of Shlomo Moussaieff, Herzliya
and London

(p. 134)
Multi-handled vessel with crosses
Provenance unknown, 5th–6th century
Glass, H 22
Collection of Shlomo Moussaieff, Herzliya
and London

(p. 135)
Mold-blown jugs with alternating crosses
and lozenges
Jerusalem, 6th–7th century
Glass, H 15
Collection of Shlomo Moussaieff, Herzliya
and London

(p. 136)
Bottle with crosses
Provenance unknown, 5th–6th century
Glass, H 19
Collection of Shlomo Moussaieff, Herzliya
and London

Oil lamp with crosses
Provenance unknown, 5th–6th century
Glass, D 10.5
Collection of Shlomo Moussaieff, Herzliya
and London

(p. 137)
Mirror-plaque against the Evil Eye, with
crosses, birds, and flowers
Provenance unknown, Byzantine period
Painted plaster, D 13
The Israel Museum, Jerusalem, 74.17.227

Mirror-plaque against the Evil Eye, with
human figures and crosses
Provenance unknown, Byzantine period
Painted plaster, L 13
The Israel Museum, Jerusalem, 74.17.228

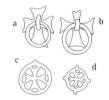

Doorknob in the shape of a ring attached
to a cross (a)
Western Wall excavations, Jerusalem,
Byzantine period
Bronze, H of cross 9.5
Israel Antiquities Authority, 99-3898
Mazar 1998, 9 (Hebrew)

Doorknob in the shape of a ring attached
to a cross (b)
Beth Shean, Byzantine period
Bronze, H of cross 8.5
Israel Antiquities Authority, 99-1574

Cross in a ring, used as an inlay or as a
scepter head (c)
Church at Shavei Ziyyon, Byzantine
period
Bronze, D 8
Israel Antiquities Authority, 55-70
Prausnitz 1967, pl. XVIII:d

Cross in a ring, used as an inlay (d)
Ramat Rachel, Byzantine period
Bronze, D 5.5
Israel Antiquities Authority, 64-1275

(p. 138)
Seal impression with a cross
Ziqim, Byzantine period
Lead, D 1.8
Israel Antiquities Authority, 56-939

Seal impression with a human figure
Beth Shean, Byzantine period
Lead, D 2
Israel Antiquities Authority, 2000-460

Round weight with a cross (a)
The weight indicated: one libra
Beth Shean, 5th–7th century
Bronze, D 6
Israel Antiquities Authority, 52-152

Octagonal weight with a cross (b)
The weight indicated: two ounces
Northern church at Nizzana,
5th–7th century
Bronze, L 3.2
Israel Antiquities Authority, 36.1284

Square weight with a cross (c)
The weight indicated: six ounces
Horvat Ara, Negev, 5th–7th century
Bronze, L. 4
Israel Antiquities Authority, 43.181

Square weight with a cross inside
an arch (d)
The weight indicated: two ounces
Beth Shean, 5th–7th century
Bronze, L 3
Israel Antiquities Authority, 52-153

Square weight with a cross inside
an arch (e)
The weight indicated: three ounces
Beth Shean, 5th–6th century
Bronze, L. 3.3
Israel Antiquities Authority, 52-154

(p. 139)
Hoard of 50 gold coins found in an oil lamp
Horvat Qav, near Carmiel, second half of
7th century
Gold and pottery, L of lamp 10
Israel Antiquities Authority, 91-2000
(lamp), 28457–28506 (coins)
Gorin-Rosen and Stern 1993

(p. 140)

Cross-pendant inlaid with wood from the
"True Cross" (a)
Mamilla district, Jerusalem, 7th century
Bronze and wood, H 5.3
Israel Antiquities Authority, 97-9004

Cross-pendant (b)
Mamilla district, Jerusalem, 6th–7th century
Bronze, L 4
Israel Antiquities Authority, 97-1158

Cross-pendant with Greek inscriptions (c)
On one side, the words "Light" and "Life";
on the other "Holy," abbreviation of the
name of Jesus, and the letters *alpha* and
omega
Mamilla district, Jerusalem, 6th–7th century
Bronze, H 3.7
Israel Antiquities Authority, 97-1157

Cross-pendant with circles (d)
Mamilla district, Jerusalem,
6th–7th century
Bronze, H 2.3
Israel Antiquities Authority, 97-1159

(p. 141)
Brooch with a cross-flower
Provenance unknown, 5th–7th century
Gold inlaid with glass and shell, L 2.5
Collection of Shlomo Moussaieff, Herzliya
and London

Brooch with a cross
Northern church at Nizzana,
5th–7th century
Bronze inlaid with glass, D 6
Israel Antiquities Authority, 36.1404
Colt 1962, 53, pl. 23:2

Cross-pendants
Provenance unknown, 6th century
Stone, H 2.4–3
Musée Sainte-Anne, Pérès Blancs,
Jerusalem, PB 3277-79

Fragment of a cross-pendant
Horvat Hur, Northern Negev,
6th century
Stone, L 2
Israel Antiquities Authority, 98-2780
Wollach 1999, fig. 182

Cross-pendant with birds
Eastern Mediterranean, 6th–7th century
Gold inlaid with blue glass
Collection of Christian Schmidt,
Munich, 402
Wamser and Zahlhaas 1998, no. 25

(p. 142)
Cross-pendants with circles
Tombs at Tarshiha and el-Makr in the
Galilee, Beth Shean, Ramle, and Shoham,
6th–7th century
Bronze, H c. 3
Israel Antiquities Authority, 31.317,
49-1053, 49-1105, 70-1997, 98-2495, 99-
3863, 99-3868

(p. 143)

Cross-pendant (a)
Tell Hadid, 6th century
Silver, H 3.3
Israel Antiquities Authority, 99-1789

Cross-pendant (b)
Shoham, 6th century
Silver, H 3.5
Israel Antiquities Authority, 98-4057

Chain with a cross (c)
Hagosherim, Upper Galilee, 4th century
Gold, L 8.6
Israel Antiquities Authority, 65-1283

Pendant with a cross (d)
Provenance unknown, 4th–5th century
Glass, H 2.5
Israel Antiquities Authority, 42.350

Pendant with a cross (e)
Shoham, 6th century
Lead, D 3
Israel Antiquities Authority, 98-2496

(p. 144)
Tombstone with a cross and a Greek
inscription
Northern church at Nizzana, Negev,
605 CE
Stone, H 117.5
Israel Antiquities Authority, 36.1375
Colt 1962, 140, no. 13; Di Segni 1997,
no. 34

Coffin with crosses
Beit Safafa, near Jerusalem, 4th century
Lead, L 89
Israel Antiquities Authority, 52-801
Rahmani 1999a, no. 82

(p. 145)
Tombstone with a cross
Haluza, Negev, Byzantine period
Stone, H 40
Israel Antiquities Authority, 91-6050

Tombstone with a cross and the first
letters of the Greek alphabet
Haluza, Negev, Byzantine period
Stone, H 33
Israel Antiquities Authority, 91-6019

Tombstone with a rosette-shaped cross
Inscribed with the name "Aaona" in Greek
Rehovot-in-the-Negev, 6th century
Stone, H 69
Israel Antiquities Authority, 77-98
Tsafrir 1984, 392 (Hebrew)

(p. 146)
Statue of a shepherd carrying a lamb
Vicinity of Gaza, 4th–5th century
Marble, H 62.5
Israel Antiquities Authority, 32.1802
Ilan 2000, 86; Tsafrir 1984, 391 (Hebrew)

(p. 148)
Plaque depicting the Annunciation
Provenance unknown, 5th century
Copper, D 14
Collection of Christian Schmidt,
Munich, 854
Wamser and Zahlhaas 1998, no. 18

Pendant (enkolpion) with depictions of the
Annunciation and the Baptism
Provenance unknown, 5th–6th century
Gold, D 7.5
Israel Antiquities Authority, 40.216
Iliffe 1950

Ampulla with a depiction of the
Annunciation
Provenance unknown, 6th century
Pottery, H 10
Israel Antiquities Authority, 65-434
Rahmani 1966, 71–74, pl. 8

(p. 149)
Token with a depiction of the
Annunciation
Caesarea, 6th century
Silver, D 2.7
Israel Antiquities Authority, 67-2272
Frova 1965, 238–41, figs. 298–99

(p. 150)
Figurine of a woman and infant
Provenance unknown, 4th–5th century
Pottery, H 12
Collection of Shlomo Moussaieff, Herzliya
and London

Figurine of a woman nursing an infant
Beth Shean, 4th–5th century
Pottery, H 12.5
Israel Antiquities Authority, P.1381
Weitzman 1979, no. 167

(p. 151)
Bracelet (see description of p. 162)

(p. 152)
Funerary stele with a depiction of a
mother and child and crosses
Egypt, 4th–5th century
Painted and incised limestone, H 55
Staatliche Museen zu Berlin,
Skulpturensammlung und Museum für
Byzantinische Kunst, 4726
Effenberger 1977, 156–68; Effenberger
and Severin 1992, no. 66

(p. 153)
Plaque with a depiction of Mary and the
infant Jesus enthroned
Syria, 6th century
Lead, D 7
Dumbarton Oaks, Washington, D.C.,
50.11
Ross 1962, no. 86

Eulogia token with a depiction of Mary
and the infant Jesus enthroned
Syria, 6th century
Pottery, D 3.5
Royal Ontario Museum, Toronto
986.181.81
Maguire et al. 1989, no. 128

Eulogia stamp with a depiction of Mary
and the infant Jesus enthroned and a
Greek inscription
Deir Dusawi, Western Negev,
6th century
Pottery, D 10
Israel Antiquities Authority, 70-5196
Rahmani 1970, 105–8, pl. 28

(p. 154)
Processional cross with a depiction of the
Adoration of the Magi, fragment
Holy Land(?), 6th century
Bronze, L 5.5
Dumbarton Oaks, Washington, D.C.,
56.18
Ross 1962, no. 65; Cotsonis 1994, no. 11

(p. 156)
Bottle with depictions of the Magi before
King Herod and the Adoration of the Magi
Eastern Mediterranean, 7th century
Brass, H 20
F.J. Dölger-Institut zur Erforschung der
Spätantike, Bonn
Engemann 1984

(p. 157)
Eulogia token with a depiction of the
Adoration of the Magi
Beth Shean, 6th–7th century
Pottery, D 5
Israel Antiquities Authority, 51-1315
Rahmani 1993, 112 (token F)

Eulogia tokens with depictions of the
Adoration of the Magi
Provenance unknown, 6th–7th century
Pottery, D 2.4, 1.9
The Israel Museum, Jerusalem,
74.34.294–295
Rahmani 1979, 34–36 (tokens A, B)

Eulogia token with a depiction of the
Adoration of the Magi
Beth Shean, 6th–7th century
Pottery, D 1.2
Israel Antiquities Authority, 93-722
Rahmani 1993, 112–13 (token G)

(p. 158)
Mold for casting metal tokens with the
figure of the Sacred Horseman and with
Mary and the infant Jesus
Provenance unknown, 6th century
Steatite, H 7
Collection of Shlomo Moussaieff, Herzliya
and London

(p. 160)
Fragment of a bracelet with the figure of
the Sacred Horseman and an inscription
in Greek: "One God who overcomes
evil," as well as the Samaritan formula:
"There is no God like Jeshurun"
Caesarea, 4th–5th century
Bronze, D of plaque 1.5
Collection of Edit Vilensky, Binyamina
Hamburger 1959

(p. 161)
Pendant-amulet with the figure of the
Sacred Horseman
Provenance unknown, 5th–6th century
Bronze, D 1.5
Collection of Shlomo Moussaieff, Herzliya
and London

Pendant-amulet with the figure of the
Sacred Horseman and a lion
Provenance unknown, 5th–6th century
Bronze, H 6
The Israel Museum, Jerusalem, 70.40.616
Gitler 1990, 371–73, fig. 3–3a

Pendant-amulet with the figure of the
Sacred Horseman
Tomb at Gush Halav, Upper Galilee,
5th–6th century
Bronze, H 6.5
Israel Antiquities Authority, 38.1091
Makhouly 1939, 49, pl. XXXII; 1h1–2

Pendant-amulet with the figure of the
Sacred Horseman
Tomb at Gush Halav, Upper Galilee,
5th–6th century
Bronze, H 6
Israel Antiquities Authority, 39.702

Ring with the figure of the Sacred
Horseman stabbing a snake with a spear
Caesarea, 6th–7th century
Bronze, D 3
Israel Antiquities Authority, 57-812
Rahmani 1985, 177, no.14

Ring with the figure of the Sacred
Horseman
Mishmar Haemeq, 6th–7th century
Bronze, D 2.3
Israel Antiquities Authority, 58-393
Rahmani 1985, 177, no. 13

(p. 162)
Bracelet with Christian scenes and a
Greek inscription
Provenance unknown, 6th century
Bronze, D 7.5
Collection of the Wolff Family, Jerusalem

Bracelet with Christian scenes and a
Greek inscription
Eastern Mediterranean, 6th century
Silver, D 7.7
Royal Ontario Museum, Toronto,
986.181.93
Vikan 1984, 74–75, fig. 10; Vikan 1991–92,
46, fig. 5

(p. 164)
Part of a mosaic floor with a cross, the
Greek letters *alpha* and *omega*, and an
abbreviation of the name Jesus Christ
Hazor-Ashdod, 6th century
D 120
Israel Antiquities Authority, 57-1347/10
Ovadiah 1987, 67–69, pl. LXXVIII:2

(p. 165)
Pendant-amulet with a depiction of the
Raising of Lazarus and inscriptions in
Greek and Aramaic
Provenance unknown, 6th century
Slate, H 4.7
The Israel Museum, Jerusalem, 70.42.617
Gitler 1990, 369–70, figs. 2–2a

Pendant-amulet with the first letters of
Psalm 91 and the figure of the Sacred
Horseman
Provenance unknown, 6th century
Bronze, H 2.5
Collection of Shlomo Moussaieff, Herzliya
and London

Pendant-amulet with a depiction of the
Raising of Lazarus
Provenance unknown, 6th century
Limonite, H. 4
Collection of Shlomo Moussaieff, Herzliya
and London

Oil lamp bearing Greek inscriptions:
"Blessing of the Mother of God,"
"Inscription of Johannes"
Provenance unknown, Byzantine period
Pottery, D 8
The Israel Museum, Jerusalem, Louis and
Carmen Warschaw Collection, 76.6.1382
Israeli and Avida 1988, no. 488

Oil lamp with a palm branch and a Greek
inscription: "The light of Christ shines
beautifully for all"
Provenance unknown, Byzantine period
Pottery, L 11
The Israel Museum, Jerusalem, Louis and
Carmen Warschaw Collection, 76.6.1396
Israeli and Avida 1988, no. 427

IV
Monasticism in the Holy Land

(p. 172)
Oil lamp on a stand with a Greek
dedicatory inscription mentioning St. Sabas
Church (or monastery) at Khirbet el-
Shubeika, Western Galilee, 6th century
Bronze, H 30
Israel Antiquities Authority, 99-3155
Aviam 1995, 55 (Hebrew)

(p. 173)
Tombstone with a Greek inscription:
"Private tomb of Sa(muel) Bishop of the
Georgians and of the monastery which
they bought in the Tower of David"
Vicinity of the Tower of David, Jerusalem,
5th–6th century
Stone, H 84
Israel Antiquities Authority, 34.897
Iliffe 1935, 78–80, pl. 48:3

(p. 176)
Tombstone of the head of the monastery
of Martyrius
Greek inscription: "Tomb of Paul, priest
and archimandrite"
Monastery of Martyrius, Maale Adumim,
6th century
Red stone, H 91
Staff Archaeological Officer in the Civil
Administration of Judea and Samaria,
K29224
Magen and Talgam 1990, fig. 1

(p. 180)
Dining utensils
Refectory, monastery of Martyrius, Maale
Adumim, 6th century
Pottery
Staff Archaeological Officer in the Civil
Administration of Judea and Samaria
Magen and Hizmi 1985, 80 (Hebrew)

(p. 181)
Dining utensils and a table
Refectory, monastery of Martyrius, Maale
Adumim, 6th century
Marble and pottery, L 114.5
Staff Archaeological Officer in the Civil
Administration of Judea and Samaria,
K28891
Magen and Hizmi 1985, 80 (Hebrew)

Round, multi-lobed table and a jug
Refectory, monastery of Martyrius, Maale
Adumim, 6th century
Bituminous stone and pottery, D 92
Staff Archaeological Officer in the Civil
Administration of Judea and Samaria,
K28900
Magen and Talgam 1990, 109, fig. 23

(p. 182)
Folio from *Acts of the Apostles*, the New
Testament, written in Christo-Palestinian
Aramaic (Syriac)
Monastery of Castellion, Judean Desert,
6th century
Parchment, L 19.5
Israel Antiquities Authority, 472121-P
Perrot 1963

(p. 184)
Human skeleton wrapped in chains
Tomb at Horvat Tabalia, southern
Jerusalem, Byzantine period
Iron, L of chain ca. 6 meters,
Weight ca. 6 kg
Collection of the Greek Orthodox
Patriarchate, Jerusalem
Kogan-Zehavi 1998

V
Pilgrimage to the Holy Places

(p. 186)
Ampulla with scenes from the life of Jesus
(see description of p. 200)

(p. 192)
Greek dedicatory inscription with a cross
Nea Church, Jewish Quarter, Jerusalem,
524/5 CE
Plaster, H 147
Israel Antiquities Authority, 77-250
Avigad 1977

(p. 196)
Part of a mosaic floor with a Greek
inscription
Mamilla district, Jerusalem, 7th century
Stone, L 180
Israel Antiquities Authority, 95-2498/1
Reich 1996, 29

Part of a mosaic floor with an Armenian
dedicatory inscription
Armenian monastery near the Damascus
Gate, Jerusalem, 7th century
Stone, D 120
Israel Antiquities Authority, 95-464/1
Amit and Wolff 1994, 296

(p. 200)
Ampulla with scenes from the life of Jesus
Jerusalem(?), 6th–7th century
Lead, D 4.6
Dumbarton Oaks, Washington, D.C.,
48.18
Ross 1962, no. 87

Ampulla with scenes from the life of Jesus
Jerusalem(?), 6th–7th century
Lead, D 4.5
F.J. Dölger-Institut zur Erforschung der
Spätantike, Bonn, 132
Engemann 1973, pl. 1

(p. 202)
Ampulla with a depiction of a saint on a
column
Caesarea, Byzantine period
Pottery, H 10.5
Israel Antiquities Authority, 99-4430
Patrich 1996, figs. 27–28; Patrich,
forthcoming

Ampulla
Excavations outside the Jaffa Gate,
Jerusalem, Byzantine period
Pottery, H 6.5
Israel Antiquities Authority, 98-3816
Maeir and Strauss 1995

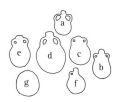

Undecorated ampulla (a)
Beth Shean, 5th–6th century(?)
Pottery, H 8
Israel Antiquities Authority, 99-3783

Ampulla with circles (b)
Ramat Rachel, Byzantine period
Pottery, H 9.5
Israel Antiquities Authority, 67-1173/1
Magness 1993, 259

Ampulla with a cross (c)
Bathhouse at Hammat Tiberias,
Byzantine period
Pottery, H 7
Israel Antiquities Authority, 56-1715

Ampulla with a cross, two birds, and
amphorae (d)
Tomb at Einabus, Samaria,
Byzantine period
Pottery, H 13.5
Israel Antiquities Authority, 42.95
Martin Nagy et al. 1996, no. 86

Ampulla with a cross-flower (e)
Lebanon, Byzantine period
Pottery, H 10.5
Musée Sainte-Anne, Pérès Blancs,
Jerusalem, PB3641

Undecorated ampulla (f)
Provenance unknown, Byzantine period
Pottery, H 7.5
Musée Sainte-Anne, Pérès Blancs,
Jerusalem, PB 3642

Ampulla with three arches, a cross, a bird,
and a Greek inscription: "Lord, have
mercy" (g)
Provenance unknown, Byzantine period
Pottery, H 8
Israel Antiquities Authority, P.1335

(p. 203)
Ampulla with a depiction of St. Menas
Provenance unknown, Byzantine period
Pottery, H 14
Israel Antiquities Authority, 71-5074

Ampulla with a depiction of St. Menas
Caesarea, Byzantine period
Pottery, H 11
Israel Antiquities Authority, 99-4429
Patrich 1996, fig. 26; Patrich, forthcoming

Bottles and jugs with depictions of
crosses or figures on columns
Provenance unknown, Byzantine period
Glass, H 8-16
Collection of Shlomo Moussaieff, Herzliya
and London

(p. 204)
Jugs with human faces
Provenance unknown, 5th–6th century
Glass, H 18-19
Collection of Shlomo Moussaieff, Herzliya
and London

(p. 205)
Head-shaped bottle with a cross on
the base
Provenance unknown, 4th century
Glass, H 9
The Israel Museum, Jerusalem, 90.24.111

Head-shaped bottle with a Christogram
on the base
Provenance unknown, 5th century
Glass, H 8
Israel Antiquities Authority, 42.11

Head-shaped bottle with crosses
Provenance unknown, Byzantine period
Glass, H 9
Collection of Shlomo Moussaieff, Herzliya
and London

(p. 206)
Eulogia jar with crosses
Provenance unknown, late 6th –
early 7th century
Glass, H 7
The Israel Museum, Jerusalem, 77.40.1005
Gift of Leo Mildenberg, Zurich

(p. 207)
Eulogia juglet
Western Wall excavations, Jerusalem,
7th century
Pottery, H 10
Israel Antiquities Authority, 78-2181
Mazar 1998, 38 (Hebrew)

Eulogia juglet
Monastery near the Damascus Gate,
Jerusalem, 7th century
Pottery, H 9
Israel Antiquities Authority, 2000-194

Miniature ampullae
Provenance unknown, Byzantine period
Lead, H approximately 4
Musée Sainte-Anne, Pérès Blancs,
Jerusalem, PB 3645-3650
Collection of Christian Schmidt, Munich
Collection of the Wolff Family, Jerusalem

Miniature ampulla with a fish and an
inscription (a)
Provenance unknown, Byzantine period
Lead, H 3.5
The Israel Museum, Jerusalem, 99.221.67

Ampulla (b)
Siloam(?), Jerusalem, Byzantine period
Lead, H 8.5
The Israel Museum, Jerusalem, 90.24.414

(p. 208)

Head-shaped jug (a)
Beth Shean, 5th–6th century(?)
Pottery, H 25
Israel Antiquities Authority 99-3839

Juglet with a face motif, used for
pouring oil (b)
Gezer, Byzantine period
Pottery, H 11.5
Israel Antiquities Authority, P.1334

Juglet with a cross-flower, used for
pouring oil (c)
Provenance unknown, Byzantine period
Pottery, H 17.5
Collection of Shlomo Moussaieff, Herzliya
and London

Juglet with a face motif, used for
pouring oil (d)
Provenance unknown, Byzantine period
Pottery, H 10.5
Israel Antiquities Authority, 71-5073

Juglet with a face motif, used for
pouring oil (e)
Provenance unknown, Byzantine period
Pottery, H 13
Israel Antiquities Authority, 71-5072

(p. 209)

Oil lamp with two wick holes and a
handle in the shape of a human figure (a)
Provenance unknown, Byzantine period
Pottery, L 11.5
The Israel Museum, Jerusalem, Louis and
Carmen Warshaw Collection, 76.6.1375
Israeli and Avida 1988, no. 433

Oil lamp with a cross and four dots on
the handle (b)
Provenance unknown, Byzantine period
Pottery, L 15
The Israel Museum, Jerusalem, Louis and
Carmen Warshaw Collection, 76.6.1380
Israeli and Avida 1988, no. 432

Oil lamp with a face on the handle (c)
Provenance unknown, Byzantine period
Pottery, L 12
Collection of Shlomo Moussaieff, Herzliya
and London

Oil lamp with faces, figures, and crosses (d)
Provenance unknown, 5th–6th century
Pottery, L 9
Israel Antiquities Authority, 76.6.1358
Israeli and Avida 1988, no. 435

(p. 210)
Bowl with 80 *eulogia* tokens bearing a
variety of Christian scenes
Syria-Palestine, 6th–7th century
Glass, D 17
Trustees of the British Museum, London,
1973, 5-1, 81
Camber 1976, fig.1; Vikan 1984, 81–83

(p. 212)
Eulogia token with a depiction of the
Entry to Jerusalem
Greek inscription: "St. Sergius"
Provenance unknown, Byzantine period
Pottery, D 4
Collection of Shlomo Moussaieff, Herzliya
and London

Eulogia token with a depiction of a saint
on a column
Provenance unknown, Byzantine period
Pottery, D 3
Collection of Shlomo Moussaieff, Herzliya
and London

Eulogia token with a depiction of the
Apparition of Jesus on the
road to Emmaus
Beth Shean, mid-6th – early 7th century
Pottery, D 4
Israel Antiquities Authority, 52-126
Rahmani 1993, 112 (token E)

Eulogia token with a depiction of the
Adoration of the Magi
Beth Shean, mid-6th – early 7th century
Pottery, D 4
Israel Antiquities Authority, 52-50
Rahmani 1993, 109–10 (token A)

Eulogia token with a depiction of the
Ascension
Beth Shean, mid-6th – early 7th century
Pottery, D 4
Israel Antiquities Authority, 52-123
Rahmani 1993, 111 (token D)

Eulogia token with a depiction of
the Baptism
Sebaste, Samaria, mid-6th –
early 7th century
Pottery, D 3.5
Israel Antiquities Authority, 47.3525
Rahmani 1980

Bibliography

Quotations from the pilgrims' writings are excerpted from Wilkinson 1977 and 1981.

Acconci, A.
1998   "Elements of the Liturgical Furniture." In M. Piccirillo and E. Alliata (eds.), *Mount Nebo: New Archaeological Excavations 1967–1997*, Jerusalem, 468–532.

Aharoni et al.
1975   "Ausgrabungen auf Hirbet el-Msas." *Zeitschrift des Deutscher Palästina-Vereins* 91, 109–30.

Akten XII.
1995   *Akten des XII. Internationalen Kongresses für Christliche Archäologie, Bonn, 22.–28.September 1991. (Jahrbuch für Antike und Christentum, Ergänzungsband 20.1, 20.2.)*

Amit, D., and S. Wolff
1994   "An Armenian Monastery in the Morasha Neighborhood, Jerusalem." In Geva (ed.) 1994, 293–98.

Anati, E.
1957   "Susita." *Publication of the Israel Antiquities Department* 5–6, 31–33, pl. 4:d. Hebrew.

Aviam, M.
1990   "Horvat Hesheq: A Unique Church in Upper Galilee: Preliminary Report." In Bottini, Di Segni, and Alliata (eds.) 1990, Jerusalem, 351–78.
1994   "The Christian Settlement in Western Galilee in the Byzantine Period." M.A. thesis, The Hebrew University of Jerusalem. Hebrew.
1995   "Remains of Churches and Monasteries in Western Galilee." *Qadmoniot* 109, 47–59. Hebrew.
1999   "Galilee through the Centuries: Confluence of Cultures." In E. M. Meyers (ed.), *Christian Galilee in the Byzantine Period*, Winona Lake, Ind., 281–300.

Avigad, A.
1977   "A Building Inscription of the Emperor Justinian and the Nea in Jerusalem." *Israel Exploration Journal* 27, 145–51.

Avi-Yonah, M.
1955   "Christian Archaeology in Israel, 1948–1954." *Christian News from Israel* 5 (3–4), 20–26. Jerusalem.

Avner, T.
1999   "Early Byzantine Wall-Paintings from Caesarea." In K. G. Holum, A. Raban, and J. Patrich (eds.), *Caesarea Papers 2*, Journal of Roman Archaeology Supplementary Series 35, 108–28.

Bagatti, B.
1939   *Guida al Museo.* Studio Biblico Francescano, Jerusalem.
1948   *Il Santuario della Visitatione ad 'Ain Karim (Montana Judaeae)*, Jerusalem.
1956–57 "Gli Altari Paleo-Cristiani della Palestina." *Liber Annuus* 7, 64–94.
1979   *Antichi Villaggi Cristiani di Samaria*, Jerusalem.

Barag, D.
1970   "Glass Pilgrim Vessels from Jerusalem. Part I." *Journal of Glass Studies* 12, 35–63.
1971   "Glass Pilgrim Vessels from Jerusalem. Parts II, III." *Journal of Glass Studies* 13, 45–63.

Barag, D., and J. Wilkinson
1974–75 "The Monza-Bobbio Flasks and the Holy Sepulchre." *Levant* 6–7, 179–87.

Baramki, D. C.
1934   "An Early Christian Basilica at 'Ein Hanniya." *Quarterly of the Department of Antiquities in Palestine* 3, 113–17.

Barash, M.
1986   "An Early Byzantine Relief at Hanita." In M. Yedaya (ed.), *The Western Galilee Antiquities*, Defense Ministry, Tel Aviv, 474–80. Hebrew.

Bar-Natan, R., and G. Mazor
1992   "The Bet Shean Excavation Project (1989–1991), Tel Iztabba." *Excavations and Surveys in Israel* 11, 50–51.

Batz, S.
     Israel Museum Journal Supplement. Forthcoming.

Ben-Pechat, M.
1989   "The Paleochristian Baptismal Fonts in the Holy Land: Formal and Functional Study." *Liber Annuus* 39, 165–88.

Biddle, M.
1999   *The Tomb of Christ*, Phoenix.

Billod, C.
1987   "Les encensoirs syro-palestiniens de Bâle." *Antike Kunst* 30, 39–56.

Bottini, G. C., L. Di Segni, and E. Alliata (eds.)
1990   *Christian Archaeology in the Holy Land. New Discoveries (Essays in Honour of Virgilio C. Corbo)*, Studium Biblicum Franciscanum Collectio Maior 36, Jerusalem.

Boyd, S. A., and M. Mango
1992   *Ecclesiastical Silver Plate in 6th Century Byzantium*, Washington.

Cabrol, F., and H. Leclerq
1907–53 *Dictionnaire de l'Archéologie chrétienne et de liturgie*, 15 vols., Paris.

Camber, R.
1976   "A Hoard of Terracotta Amulets from the Holy Land." *Actes du XVe Congrès International d'Etudes Byzantines, Athens – September 1976*, Athens, 99–106.

Campbell, S. D.
1985   *The Malcove Collection. A Catalogue of the Objects in the Lillian Malcove Collection of the University of Toronto*, Toronto.

Casson, L., and E. Hettich
1950   *Excavations at Nessana 2. Literary Papyri*, Princeton.

Chalkia, E.
1991   *Le Mense Paleocristiane. Tipologia e Funzioni delle Mense nel Culto Paleocristiano*, Vatican City.

Chitty, D. J.
1966   *The Desert a City. An Introduction to the Study of Egyptian and Palestinian Monasticism under the Christian Empire*, Oxford.

Cohen, R.
1993   "A Byzantine Church and Its Mosaic Floors at Kissufim." In Tsafrir (ed.) 1993, 277–82.

Colt, H. D. (ed.)
1962   *Excavations at Nessana 1*, London.

Cotsonis, J. A.
1994   *Byzantine Figural Processional Crosses*, Washington.

Couasnon, C.
1974   *The Church of the Holy Sepulchre in Jerusalem*, London.

Cré, R. P. L.
1904   "Epitaphe de la Diaconesse Sophie." *Revue Biblique*, 260–61.

Crowfoot, J. W.
1941   *Early Churches in Palestine*, London.

Crowfoot, J. W., G. M. Crowfoot, and R. M. Kenyon
1957   *The Objects from Samaria*, London.

Dahari, U.
1998   "Horbat Tinshemet, Church of St. Bacchus." *Excavations and Surveys in Israel* 19, 67*–68*.

Dahari, U., and U. Ad
2000   "Shoham Bypass Road." *Excavations and Surveys in Israel* 20, 56*–59*.

Dalton, O. M.
1901   *Catalogue of Early Christian Antiquities and Objects from the Christian East in the British Museum*, London.

Dauphin, C.
1983   "On the Pilgrim's Way to the Holy City." *Bulletin of the Anglo-Israel Archaeological Society* 1982–83, 25–31.
1993a   "A Byzantine Ecclesiastical Farm at Shlomi." In Tsafrir (ed.) 1993, 43–48.
1993b   "Dora-Dor: A Station for Pilgrims in the Byzantine Period on Their Way to Jerusalem." In Tsafrir (ed.) 1993, 90–97.

Dauphin, C., and G. Edelstein
1984   *L'Eglise Byzantine de Naharyia (Israel). Etude Archéologique*, Thessaloniki.
1993   "The Byzantine Church at Nahariya." In Tsafrir (ed.) 1993, 49–53.

Delougaz, P., and R. C. Haines
1960   *A Byzantine Church at Khirbat Al-Kerak*, Chicago.

Di Segni, L.
1997   "Dated Greek Inscriptions from Palestine from the Roman and Byzantine Periods." Ph.D. diss., The Hebrew University of Jerusalem.

Donceel-Voute, P.
1995   "Le rôle des reliquaires dans les pèlerinages." In *Akten XII*. 1995, 184–205.

Duval, N.
1994   "L'Architecture chrétienne et les pratiques liturgiques en Jordanie en rapport avec la Palestine: Recherches Nouvelles." In K. Painter (ed.), *'Churches Built in Ancient Times': Recent Studies in Early Christian Archaeology*, London, 150–212.

Effenberger, A.
1977   "Die Grabstele aus Medinet el-Fajum. Zum Bild der stillenden Gottesmutter in der koptischen Kunst." In *Forschungen und Berichte*. (Staatliche Museen zu Berlin 18, 158–68.)

Effenberger, A., and H. G. Severin
1992   *Das Museum für Spätantike und Byzantinische Kunst*, Staatliche Museen zu Berlin, Mainz.

Elbern, V. H.
1972–74 "Zur Morphologie der Bronzenen Weihrauchgefässe aus Palestina." *Archivo Español de Arqveologia* 45–47 (125–130), 447–62.

Engemann, J.
1972   "Anmerkungen zu spätantiken Geräten des Alltagslebens mit Christlichen Bildern, Symbolen und Inschriften." *Jahrbuch für Antike und Christentum* 15, 154–73.
1973   "Palästinensische Pilgerampullen im F. J. Dölger-Institut in Bonn." *Jahrbuch für Antike und Christentum* 16, 5–27.

1984   "Eine spätantike Messingkanne mit zwei Darstellungen aus der Magiererzählung im F. J. Dölger-Institut in Bonn." In *Vivarium. Festschrift Theodor Klauser zum 90. Geburtstag. (Jahrbuch für Antike und Christentum*, Ergänzungsband 11, 115–31.)
1995   "Eulogien und Votive." In *Akten XII*. 1995, 223–33.

Feig, N.
1994   "A Byzantine Bread Stamp from Tiberias." *Liber Annuus* 44, 591–94.

Figueras, P.
1985   *Byzantine Inscriptions from Beer-Sheva and the Negev*, Museum of the Negev, Beersheva.
1995   "Pilgrims to Sinai in the Byzantine Negev." In *Akten XII*. 1995, 756–62.

Finegan, J.
1969   *The Archaeology of the New Testament. The Life of Jesus and the Beginning of the Early Church*, Princeton.

Fitzgerald, G. M.
1931   *Beth-Shan Excavations 1921–1923. The Arab and Byzantine Levels*, Philadelphia.
1939   *A Sixth Century Monastery at Beth-Shan (Scythopolis)*, Philadelphia.

Flusser, D.
1994   *Jewish Sources in Early Christianity*, Tel Aviv. Hebrew.

Frova, A.
1965   *Scavi di Caesarea Maritima*, Milan.

Galavaris, G.
1970   *Bread at the Liturgy. The Symbolism of Early Christian and Byzantine Bread Stamps*, Madison, Milwaukee, and London.

Gazit, D., and Y. Lender
1993   "The Church of St. Stephen at Horvat Be'er-shem'a." In Tsafrir (ed.) 1993, 273–76.

Geva, H. (ed.)
1994   *Ancient Jerusalem Revealed*, Jerusalem.

Gitler, H.
1990   "Four Magical and Christian Amulets." *Liber Annuus* 40, 365–74.

Gorin-Rosen, Y., and E. J. Stern
1993   "Horvat Qav." *Excavations and Surveys in Israel* 13, 17–18.

Grabar, A.
1957   *Les ampoules de Terre Sainte (Monza-Bobbio)*, Paris.

Greenhut, Z.
1992   "The 'Caiaphas' Tomb in North Talpiyot, Jerusalem." '*Atiqot* 21, 63–71.

Grigg, R. J.
1974   "The Images on the Palestinian Flasks as Possible Evidence of the Monumental Decoration of Palestinian Martyria." Ph.D. diss., University of Minnesota.

Haas, N.
1970   "Anthropological Observations on the Skeletal Remains from Giv'at ha-Mivtar." *Israel Exploration Journal* 20, 38–59.

Habas, L.
1994   "The Relief Art of Chancel Screens in Churches and Synagogues in Palestine in the Byzantine Period: A Stylistic and Iconographic Study." M.A. thesis, The Hebrew University of Jerusalem. Hebrew.
1999   "The Marble Furniture." In Hirschfeld 1999, 119–32.

Hamburger, A.
1959   "A Greco-Samaritan Amulet from Caesarea." *Israel Exploration Journal* 9, 43–45.

Hamilton, R. W.
1931   "Street Levels in the Tyropoeon Valley." *Quarterly of the Department of Antiquities in Palestine* 1, 105–10.
1974   "Thuribles: Ancient or Modern?" *Iraq* 36, 53–65.

Hauser, S. R.
1992   *Spätantike und frühbyzantinische Silberlöffel: Bemerkungen zur Produktion von Luxusgütern im 5. bis 7. Jahrhundert.* (Jahrbuch für Antike und Christentum, Ergänzungsband 19.)

Hirschfeld, Y.
1992   *The Judean Desert Monasteries in the Byzantine Period,* New Haven and London.
1999   *The Early Byzantine Monastery at Khirbet Ed-Deir in the Judean Desert: The Excavations in 1981–1987,* Qedem 38, Jerusalem.

Holum, K. G.
1995   "A Newly Discovered Martyr Church at Caesarea Maritima, Israel: Goal of Pilgrimage." In *Akten XII.* 1995, 849–54.

Hunt, E. D.
1982   *Holy Land Pilgrimage in the Later Roman Empire, AD 312–460,* Oxford.

Ilan, O.
2000   *Image and Artifact: Treasures of the Rockefeller Museum with Aerial Photographs by Duby Tal and Moni Haramati,* Jerusalem.

Iliffe, J. H.
1933a   "Rock-cut Tomb at Tarshiha." *Quarterly of the Department of Antiquities in Palestine* 3, 9–16.
1933b   "A Tomb at El Bassa." *Quarterly of the Department of Antiquities in Palestine* 3, 81–91.
1935   "Cemeteries and a 'Monastery' at the Y.M.C.A., Jerusalem." *Quarterly of the Department of Antiquities in Palestine* 4, 70–80.
1950   "A Byzantine Gold Enkolpion from Palestine (About Sixth Century A.D.)." *Quarterly of the Department of Antiquities in Palestine* 14, 97–99.

Inscriptions Reveal
1973   *Inscriptions Reveal. Documents from the Time of the Bible, the Mishna and the Talmud,* The Israel Museum, Jerusalem.

Israeli, Y.
1998   *The Wonders of Ancient Glass at The Israel Museum, Jerusalem,* Jerusalem.

Israeli, Y., and U. Avida
1988   *Oil Lamps from Eretz Israel. The Louis and Carmen Warschaw Collection at the Israel Museum,* Jerusalem.

Kirk, G. E.
1936   "Era Problems in the Greek Inscriptions of the Southern Desert." *The Journal of the Palestine Oriental Society* 17, 209–17.

Klausen-Nottmeyer, B.
1995   "Eulogien – Transport und Weitergabe von Segenskraft. Ergebnisse einer Zusammenstellung von Pilgerandenken." In *Akten XII.* 1995, 922–27.

Kogan-Zehavi, E.
1998   "The Tomb and Memorial of a Chain-wearing Anchorite at Khirbet Tabaliya, near Jerusalem." *'Atiqot* 35, 135–48.

Kötzche, L.
1995   "Das Heilige Grab in Jerusalem und seine Nachfolge." In *Akten XII.* 1995, 272–90.

Kötzche-Breitenbruch, L.
1984   "Pilgerandenken aus dem Heiligen Land. Drei Neuerwerbungen des Württembergischen Landesmuseums in Stuttgart." In *Vivarium. Festschrift Theodor Klauser zum 90. Geburstag.* (Jahrbuch für Antike und Christentum, Ergänzungsband 11, 229–46.)

Kraemer, C. J., Jr.
1958   *Excavations at Nessana 3. Non-Literary Papyri,* Princeton.

Leibovitch, J.
1953   "The Reliquary Column of Dor." *Christian News in Israel* 5, 22–23.
1957   "Dor." *Publication of the Israel Antiquities Department* 5–6, 35, pl. 5:b. Hebrew.

Licht, J.
1956   "The Doctrine of the Thanksgiving Scroll, I–II." *IEJ* 6 (1–2), 1–13, 89–101.

Limor, O.
1998   *Holy Land Travels. Christian Pilgrims in Late Antiquity,* Jerusalem. Hebrew.

Lowrie, W.
1969   *Art in the Early Church,* New York. (1st ed. 1947.)

Maeir, A. M.
1995   "The Excavations at Mamilla, Jerusalem, Phase I." In Geva (ed.) 1994, 299–305.

Maeir, A. M., and Y. Strauss
1995   "A Pilgrim Flask of Anatolian Origin from Late Byzantine / Early Ummayyad Jerusalem." *Anatolian Studies* 45, 237–41.

Magen, Y.
1994   "Jerusalem as a Center of the Stone Vessel Industry during the Second Temple Period." In Geva (ed.) 1994, 244–56.

Magen, Y., and H. Hizmi
1985   "The Monastery of Martyrius at Ma'ale Adummim." *Qadmoniot,* 71–72, 62–92. Hebrew.

Magen, Y., and R. Talgam
1990   "The Monastery of Martyrius at Ma'ale Adummim (Khirbet el-Murassas) and Its Mosaics." In Bottini, Di Segni, and Alliata (eds.) 1990, 91–152.

Magness, J.
1993   *Jerusalem Ceramic Chronology circa 200–800 C.E.,* Sheffield.
1996   "Blessings from Jerusalem: Evidence for Early Christian Pilgrimage." *Eretz Israel* 25, 39–45.

Maguire, E. D., et al.
1989   *Art and Holy Powers in the Early Christian House,* The Krannert Art Museum, University of Illinois.

Makhouly, N.
1939   "Rock-cut Tombs at El-Jish." *Quarterly of the Department of Antiquities in Palestine* 8, 45–50.

Mango, C.
1986   *The Art of the Byzantine Empire 312–1453. Sources and Documents,* Medieval Academy, Toronto. (1st ed. 1972.)
1995   "The Pilgrim's Motivation." In *Akten XII.* 1995, 1–9.

Mango, M. M.
1986   *Silver from Early Byzantium. The Kaper Koraon and Related Treasures,* Baltimore.

Manns, F., and E. Alliata (eds.)
1993   *Early Christianity in Context: Monuments and Documents,* Jerusalem.

Martin Nagy, R., C. L. Meyers, E. M. Meyers, and Z. Weiss (eds.)
1996   *Sepphoris in Galilee. Crosscurrents of Culture,* Winona Lake, Ind.

Mazar, E.
1998   *The Monastery of the Virgins. Byzantine Period. Temple Mount Excavations in Jerusalem*, Jerusalem. Hebrew.

Mazor, G., and R. Bar-Natan
1996   "The Bet Shean Excavation Project, Tel Iztabba." *Excavations and Surveys in Israel* 17, 30–33.

Meimaris, Y. E.
1986   *Sacred Names, Saints, Martyrs and Church Officials in the Greek Inscriptions and Papyri pertaining to the Christian Church of Palestine*, Athens.

Negev, A.
1981   *The Greek Inscriptions from the Negev*, Studium Biblicum Franciscanum Collectio Minor 25, Jerusalem.
1990   "The Cathedral of Elusa and the New Typology and Chronology of the Byzantine Churches in the Negev." *Liber Annuus* 39, 129–42.

Netzer, E.
1990   "The Byzantine Churches of Herodion." In Bottini, Di Segni, and Alliata (eds.) 1990, 165–76.

Netzer, E., R. Birger-Calderon, and A. Feller
1993   "The Churches of Herodion." In Tsafrir 1993, 219–32.

Nodet, E., and J. Taylor
1998   *The Origins of Christianity. An Exploration*, Collegeville, Minn.

Ousterhout, R. (ed.)
1990   *The Blessings of Pilgrimage*, Urbana, Ill.

Ovadiah, R., and A. Ovadiah
1987   *Hellenistic, Roman and Early Byzantine Mosaic Pavements in Israel*, Rome.

Patrich, J.
1995   *The Judean Desert Monasticism in the Byzantine Period. The Institution of Sabas and His Disciples*, Jerusalem. Hebrew.
1996   "Warehouses and Granaries in Caesarea Maritima." In A. Raban and K. G. Holum (eds.), *Caesarea Maritima*, Leiden and New York, 146–75.
            Israel Museum Journal Supplement. Forthcoming.

Patrich, J., et al.
1999   "The Warehouse Complex and Governor's Palace." In K. G. Holum, A. Raban, and J. Patrich (eds.), *Caesarea Papers 2*, Journal of Roman Archaeology Supplementary Series 35, 70–107.

Perrot, C.
1963   "Un Fragment Christo-palestinien découvert à Khirbet Mird." *Revue Biblique* 70, 506–55.

Piccirillo, M.
1979   "Un braccialetto cristiano della regione di Betlem." *Liber Annuus* 29, 244–52.
1992   "La Chiesa dei Leoni a Umm Al-Rasas – Kastron Mefaa." *Liber Annuus* 42, 199–225.
1994   "Alcuni Oggetti Liturgici Inediti del Museo della Flagellatione a Gerusalemme." In *Historiarum Pictura Refert in Honor of Alejandro Recio Veganzones*, Rome, 451–70.

Piccirillo, M., and E. Alliata
1999   *The Madaba Centenary 1897–1997*, Studium Biblicum Franciscanum Collectio Maior 40, Jerusalem.

Prausnitz, M.
1967   *Excavations at Shavei Zion*, Rome.

Rahmani, L. Y.
1964   "Mirror Plaques from a 5th Century A.D. Tomb." *Israel Exploration Journal* 14, 50–60.
1966   "Two Early Christian Ampullae." *Israel Exploration Journal* 16, 71–74.
1970   "A *Eulogia* Stamp from the Gaza Region." *Israel Exploration Journal* 20, 105–8.
1979   "The Adoration of the Magi on Two Sixth-Century C.E. *Eulogia* Tokens." *Israel Exploration Journal* 29, 34–36.
1980   "Miscellanea – Roman to Medieval: A Representation of the Baptism on an *Eulogia* Token." *'Atiqot* 14 (English Series), 109–10.
1985   "On Some Byzantine Brass Rings in the State Collections." *'Atiqot* 17 (English Series), 168–81.
1993   "*Eulogia* Tokens from Byzantine Beth-She'an." *'Atiqot* 22, 109–19.
1994   *A Catalogue of Jewish Ossuaries in the Collections of the State of Israel*, Jerusalem.
1999a   *A Catalogue of Roman and Byzantine Lead Coffins from Israel*, Jerusalem.
1999b   "The Byzantine Solomon *Eulogia* Tokens in the British Museum." *Israel Exploration Journal* 49, 92–104.

Reich, R.
1992   "Ossuary Inscriptions from the 'Caiaphas' Tomb." *'Atiqot* 21, 72–77.
1996   "'God Knows Their Names'. Mass Christian Grave Revealed in Jerusalem." *Biblical Archaeology Review* 22 (2), 26–33, 60.

Reich, R., E. Shukron, and Y. Billig
1991   "Jerusalem, Mamilla Area." *Excavations and Surveys in Israel* 10, 24–25.

Ross, M. C.
1962   *Catalogue of the Byzantine and Early Mediaeval Antiquities in the Dumbarton Oaks Collection*, Vol. 1: *Metalwork, Ceramics, Glass, Glyptics, Painting*, Washington.
1964   "Byzantine Bronze Hands Holding Crosses." *Archaeology* 17 (2), 101–3.

Safran, L. (ed.)
1998   *Heaven on Earth. Art and the Church in Byzantium*, University Park, Pennsylvania.

Saller, S. J.
1946   *Discoveries at St. John's 'Ein Karim.' 1941–1942*, Jerusalem.

Sanders, E. P.
1993   *The Historical Figure of Jesus*, London.

Segal, A.
1983   *The Byzantine City of Shivta (Esbeita), Negev Desert, Israel*, BAR International Series 179.
1988   *Architectural Decoration in Byzantine Shivta, Negev Desert, Israel*, BAR International Series 420.

Sibella, P.
1997   "Light from the Past: The 1996 Tantura Roman Lamp." *The Institute of Nautical Archaeology Quarterly* 24 (4), 16–18.

Spaer, M.
            Beads and Other Small Glass Objects in the Israel Museum Collection. Forthcoming.

Treasures
1986   *Treasures of the Holy Land*, Exhibition catalogue at the Metropolitan Museum of Art. New York.

Tsafrir, Y.
1984   *Eretz Israel from the Destruction of the Second Temple to the Muslim Conquest 2. Archaeology and Art*, Jerusalem. Hebrew.
1993   "Ancient Churches in the Holy Land." *Biblical Archaeology Review* 19 (5), 26–39.

Tsafrir, Y., et al.
1988   *Excavations at Rehovot-in-the-Negev 1: The Northern Church*, Qedem
        25, Jerusalem.

Tsafrir, Y. (ed.)
1993   *Ancient Churches Revealed*, Jerusalem.

Tsafrir, Y., and S. Safrai (eds.)
1999   *The History of Jerusalem. The Roman and Byzantine Periods
        (70–638 C.E.)*, Jerusalem. Hebrew.

Tzaferis, V.
1970   "Jewish Tombs at and near Giv'at ha-Mivtar, Jerusalem."
        Israel Exploration Journal 20, 18 32.
1971   "Christian Symbols of the 4th Century and the Church Fathers."
        Ph.D. diss., The Hebrew University of Jerusalem.

Tzaferis, V., N. Feig, A. Onn, and E. Shukron
1994   "Excavations at the Third Wall, North of the Jerusalem Old City."
        In Geva (ed.) 1994, 287–92.

Tzori, N.
1970   "Bronze Utensils from Byzantine Beth She'an." *Qadmoniot* 3:
        2 (10), 67–68. Hebrew.

Ullmann, L.
1996   "Two Ostraca with the Niceno-Constantinopolitan Creed in the
        Israel Museum." *Zeitschrift für Papyrologie und Epigraphik* 113,
        194–96.

Vikan, G.
1984   "Art, Medicine, and Magic in Early Byzantium." *Dumbarton Oaks
        Papers* 38, 65–86.
1991–92 "Two Byzantine Amuletic Armbands and the Group to which They
        Belong." *The Journal of the Walters Art Gallery*, 33–51.
1995   "Early Byzantine Pilgrimage *Devotionalia* as Evidence of the
        Appearance of Pilgrimage Shrines." In *Akten XII*. 1995, 377–88.

Vincent, H., and F.-M. Abel
1914   *Jérusalem. Recherches de Topographie, d'Archéologie et d'Histoire 2.
        Jérusalem Nouvelle*, Paris.

Vitto, F.
1984   "Horvat Bata (Karmiel) – 1984." *Excavations and Surveys in Israel* 3,
        7–8.
1995   "The Interior Decoration of Palestinian Churches and
        Synagogues." In S. Efthymiadis et al. (eds.), *Bosphorus. Essays in
        Honour of Cyril Mango.* (*Byzantinische Forschungen. Internationale
        Zeitschrift für Byzantinistik*, Band 21), 283–300.

Volbach, W. F.
1952   *Elfenbeinarbeiten der Spätantike und frühen Mittelalters*, 2d ed.,
        Römisch-Germanisches Zentralmuseum zu Mainz, Mainz.

Wamser, L., and Zahlhaas, G.
1998   *Rom und Byzanz. Archäologische Kostbarkeiten aus Bayern*, Munich.

Weitzman, K.
1974   "*Loca Sancta* and the Representational Arts of Palestine."
        Dumbarton Oaks Papers 28, 33–55.
1976   *The Monastery of Santa Catherine at Mount Sinai: The Icons*, Vol. 1:
        From 6th to 10th Century, Princeton.

Weitzman, K. (ed.)
1979   *Age of Spirituality: Late Antique and Early Christian Art, Third to
        Seventh Century*, New York.

Wilkinson, J.
1972   "The Tomb of Christ. An Outline of Its Structural History."
        Levant 4, 83–97.
1976   "Christian Pilgrims in Jerusalem during the Byzantine Period."
        Palestine Exploration Quarterly 108, 75–101.
1977   *Jerusalem Pilgrims before the Crusades*, Warminster.
1981   *Egeria's Travels to the Holy Land*, Jerusalem and London.
        (1st ed. 1971.)

Wollach, Z.
1999   "Horbat Hur." *Excavations and Surveys in Israel* 19, 89*–90*.

Wright, G. E.
1939   "The Good Shepherd." *Biblical Archaeologist* 2 (4), 44–48.

Yadin, Y.
1973   "Epigraphy and Crucifixion." *Israel Exploration Journal* 23, 18–22.

Yeivin, Z., and G. Finkielsztejn
1999   "Horbat Castra – 1993–1997." *Hadashot Arkheologiyot, Excavations
        and Surveys in Israel* 109, 23*–27*.

Youtie, H. C.
1936   "Ostraca from Sbeitah." *American Journal of Archaeology* 40,
        452–59.

Zias, J.
1985   "Anthropological Analysis of a Christian Reliquary." *Israel
        Exploration Journal* 35, 180.

Zias, J., and E. Sekeles
1985   "The Crucified Man from Giv'at ha-Mivtar: A Reappraisal." *Israel
        Exploration Journal* 35, 22–27.

Ziffer, I.
1998   *O my Dove, that art in the clefts of the rock: The Dove-allegory in
        Antiquity*, Eretz Israel Museum, Tel Aviv.

Credits for Photographs and Drawings

Photographs

© The Israel Museum, Jerusalem: 20, 22, 23 (above), 24, 33, 40, 72 (below), 73 (below), 86–87, 146, 192

© The Israel Museum, Jerusalem / by Avraham Hay: cover, 18, 20, 23 (below), 34, 42, 43, 48–49, 54, 55, 56–57, 59, 62, 68–72 (above), 73 (above), 74–76, 78, 80 (above), 81 (above), 82 (above), 84, 88, 89 (center and right), 92 (below), 96, 97, 99, 102, 104–10, 112 (above), 113, 119 (above), 120, 122, 123 (above), 124, 126, 128–32, 133 (above right and below), 134–41 (above and below left), 142–45, 148 (center and below), 149, 150, 153 (below), 157, 158, 161, 162 (above), 164, 165, 172 (above), 173, 176, 180, 181, 196 (above), 202–9, 212

© The Israel Museum, Jerusalem / by Peter Lanyi: 160

© The Israel Museum, Jerusalem / by Ilan Sztulman: 25

© The Israel Antiquities Authority: 66, 80–81 (below), 112 (below), 114–15, 125, 182, 184

© The Israel Antiquities Authority / by Nicky Davidov: frontispiece, 82–83 (below)

© Bayerisches Nationalmuseum München / Haberland: 141 (below right)

© The British Museum, London: 93, 100 (above), 119 (below), 210

© Byzantine Collection, Dumbarton Oaks, Washington, D.C.: 90 (above), 91, 153 (above center), 154, 186–87, 200 (above)

© J. Deckers, Altenmünster: 118, 148 (above)

© Prähistorische Staatssammlung München / M. Ederlein: 77, 127, 133 (above left)

© Royal Ontario Museum, Toronto: 44 (above), 85, 90 (below), 103, 151, 153 (above right), 162 (below)

© Staatliche Museen zu Berlin, Skulpturensammlung und Museum für Byzantinische Kunst: 92 (above and center), 100 (below), 152

© Staff Archaeological Officer in the Civil Administration of Judea and Samaria: 178

© University of Pennsylvania Museum of Archaeology and Anthropology, Philadelphia: 94, 95

© University of Toronto: 44 (below), 89 (left), 101

© Josef Engemann: 156, 200 (below)

© Baruch Gian: 47, 60, 61 (above), 172 (below)

© David Harris: 197

© Avraham Hay: 166–67, 170, 171, 174

© Garo Nalbandian: 26–27, 32, 65, 98, 121, 123 (below), 196 (below)

© Andrei Vainer: 61 (below)

Félix Bonfils, Israel Museum Collection, Gift of the Ministry of Foreign Affairs: 14–15

Mendel John Diness, Israel Museum Collection, Bequest of Suzanne and Marcel Chayette, Paris: 36

Underwood & Underwood, Collection of Avraham Hay: 191

Drawings

© The Israel Museum, Jerusalem: 23 (above)

© The Israel Museum, Jerusalem / by Pnina Arad: 18, 19, 23 (below), 43, 45, 91, 135, 138, 148, 149, 153, 157, 159, 161, 163, 201, 206, 212

© The Israel Museum, Jerusalem / by Balage: 38, 46 (below), 63, 194, 195, 198–99

© The Israel Antiquities Authority: 185

© The Open Museum, Tefen / by Leen Ritmeyer: 58

© Staff Archaeological Officer in the Civil Administration of Judea and Samaria / by Tanya Slutskai: 179

© Leen Ritmeyer: 22

Drawings after:

Crowfoot 1941: 52
Piccirillo 1992: 53
Rahmani 1999b: 211
Segal 1986: 60 (below)
Wilkinson 1976: 46 (above)
Yoram Tsafrir and Lea Di Segni, Tsafrir 1993: 30
Zias and Sekeles 1985: 24